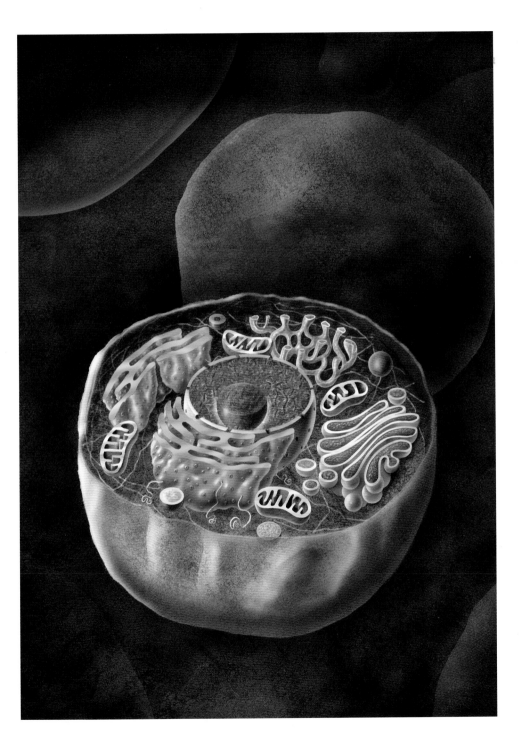

Reflections on a Decade of Dedication . . .

Invisible
MIRACLES

The Revolution in Cellular Nutrition

Dr. Myron Wentz

To my USANA family worldwide,
who are sharing the dream of
true health

A word of appreciation to Peter Van Duser and Dr. Denis Waitley, who prodded me to make time to recite these initial reflections of a decade of discovery in a lifelong journey.

Thanks also to Dr. Tim Wood, Dr. John McDonald, and my entire scientific team for their dedication to excellence during the past decade.

I also would like to recognize Lori Bothner and her creative staff at USANA, including John Cordova, Deborah Funk, Nathan Paret and Heather King, as well as Bob Derber of UNItogether, for their contributions in the design and graphics of this book.

Contents

Foreword

This book is a brief glimpse into the continuing journey of a giant of a man. A remarkable man with no formal training in business who has built several successful enterprises, one after another. A man with formal training in science who has devoted much of his career challenging and explaining the limitations of current scientific knowledge. A man from a tiny town in North Dakota who has become a global torchbearer for health and wellness. A man inspired by pioneers Dr. Linus Pauling, Dr. Jonas Salk, and Dr. Albert Schweitzer and destined, in my opinion, to be remembered as they are, for their significant contributions to the quality of human life.

Myron W. Wentz has touched and enhanced the lives of hundreds of thousands of individuals throughout the world. Many have expressed their personal testimonials concerning health improvements they have experienced as a result of following his advice. It is impossible to calculate the benefits realized by patients worldwide, whose infectious diseases have been diagnosed by clinical laboratories using tests he developed.

As his career attests, Dr. Wentz has the unique combination of success in both the practical world of business and the rarified atmosphere of medical science. This has allowed him, to some degree, the freedom to pursue his interests on his own terms.

This is not his life story, because his story, still largely
untold, continues to unfold. Nor is it a tribute to what he has
done, for he would be the first to tell you that there is so much
left to do. That he could have retired in the lap of luxury years
ago – island hopping, basking in material comforts, and pursuing
less challenging but entertaining avocations – is without question.
So what drives an individual like Myron Wentz?

I posed that question many years ago to my former
employer and mentor, Dr. Jonas Salk, the developer of the first
effective polio vaccine. His answer, then, is the answer I believe
Dr. Wentz would give if you were to ask him today:

> It is always with excitement that I wake
> up in the morning wondering what my intu-
> ition will toss up to me, like gifts from the
> sea. I do not go to my laboratory to work. I
> go to seek, to understand, to discover. I live
> to make life more worth living for those
> who will follow, thereby giving myself a
> reason for being.

As I have come to know Dr. Wentz during the past decade,
I see many similarities between my late friend and mentor, Jonas
Salk, and Myron Wentz. But there is one major difference: where-
as the research of Salk was funded by universities and later by a
major nonprofit organization, Dr. Wentz has paid his own way in
pursuing his dreams.

In introducing you to the Myron Wentz I know, I'm
reminded of a passage from a biography of the Nobel Prize winning physicist Madame Curie. Her daughter, Eve Curie, quotes
her mother:

> Humanity needs practical men, who get the most out of their work, and, without forgetting the general good, safeguard their own interests. But humanity also needs dreamers, for whom the disinterested development of an enterprise is so captivating that it becomes impossible for them to devote their care to their own material profit.[1]

I have met few individuals more generous, more approachable and more caring than Dr. Wentz; nor have I met anyone who could absorb so much information and still be hungry for more. He has learned much about life and has passed on much of what he has learned to those who would listen. He has journeyed a long way in his lifetime on the road less traveled, and those who have journeyed with him have experienced more than they ever expected was possible in one lifespan.

I am one of those who has traveled some distance with Myron Wentz, and he has taught me much about improving the quality of my own life and that of my family. I have always considered myself an optimist, but he has shown me firsthand that almost anything is possible if your desire is strong enough.

More importantly, he has been willing to go into the kitchen of bold creativity and unfettered experimentation and withstand the heat of groupthink and prejudice. He believes in true health and is seeking to discover its secrets with a passion that is as spiritual as it is scientific.

Dr. Denis Waitley
Author, *Seeds of Greatness*

Prologue

The cell – elegant, resourceful, marvelously intricate. The fundamental unit of life.

Poison it, injure it, or starve it, and the resulting damage causes degeneration and disease. Nurture it, protect it, and feed it with the nutrients it needs, and it repairs itself, providing health and longevity.

All of us begin as a single cell. That one cell divides into two, two into four, and so on, with the newly generated cells programmed to perform specific missions throughout our lives. The trillions of cells work in synergy within the universe we call our body. Every day, billions of new cells are produced to replace those that have served before them. This natural process is constantly under attack by the environment – toxins in the soil and water, pollutants in the air, radiation from the sun, preservatives in our processed food, and oxidative stress in our daily lives and lifestyle choices.

Understanding these causes and effects and beginning to learn how to take a proactive approach to health and wellness are the core objectives of this book. It would take volumes of scientific writings and years of careful study to come to know the impact of cellular nutrition on the quality and longevity of our lives. I can only scratch the surface to give you a few insights into the progress we have witnessed during the past decade and share with you a vision of hope for what lies ahead in the decades to come.

Cells are virtually unknown, undervalued, and misunderstood by most of us. They are taken for granted as just being there, unseen and unimportant until they become uncontrollable or dysfunctional.

I have devoted much of my career as a scientist to microbiology and optimal health at the cellular level. I don't make claims about prevention and healing until the results have been clinically tested and proven. But if you knew what I know about growing healthy cells and their incredible ability to remain young, vibrant, and strong, you would appreciate them in an entirely different light.

The cells that are you are simply invisible miracles.

Chapter 1
True Health

This is a book about life. Although some aspects of my own life are included here, it is really a book about your life. This is not an autobiography. It is meant to be a reveille to urge you to become proactive rather than reactive toward your health.

Most of my journey has been devoted to learning what life is, what is required to sustain life, and how to defend against those factors that threaten life. For me, this has become an endless pursuit, all through college and years of postgraduate study and decades of additional learning, while I was creating business health-care institutions. The human body is so wonderfully complex that it seems we will never discover the last of its secrets, in spite of the progress of science at its current bewildering pace.

While the goal is still out of reach, the journey has been and continues to be challenging and exhilarating. What I have learned thus far is what true health is and is not:

True health is not simply how you feel when you wake up each morning. Nor is it a favorable lab, radiology, or physical exam report from your physician. True health is not based on the sculpture of your physique nor your ability to compete in a triathlon.

True health is being absolutely the best you can be with the conditions you were given and the situation in which you now live. True health is not just the absence of disease. It is empowering our bodies to perform at their optimum level.

When I think of optimal health, I think of energy and stamina. I think of flexibility, strength, and endurance. Optimal health means having reserves to deal with the unexpected stresses encountered in everyday life. It includes having a clear, strong mind, and a good memory. It means having a feeling of spiritual harmony and balance. It means looking forward to every new day, not looking back at the good old days.

Good health cannot and must not be taken for granted. It should be guarded, with utmost security and attention, every day of your life. That is the most effective way to avoid degenerative disease and thus to achieve the maximum number of years of active, enjoyable living. Only by maintaining good health can you do what you want to do and need to do for yourself and your loved ones.

Many of us spend our lives working hard to save money enough to enjoy the golden years, only to discover that we are going to have to spend a great deal of money and effort trying to regain the health we sacrificed in our harried pursuit of material comfort. One of the great frailties in our society, which we seldom notice, is taking too much for granted.

We tend to complain about little things and fail to recognize the opportunity we have to tap into the knowledge and abundance available to us. It is ironic that in America we seem to take health for granted. We act as if it is something owed to us, and we lament the high cost of health care and the horror stories that create malpractice suits.

Many of us think of health care after the fact, as a high-tech cure or series of treatments from a private practitioner or government agency, funded by insurance. We seldom view it as an individual responsibility. In the past we have said, "Why don't they do something to fix our health-care system?" From now on, we must say instead, "Here's what I am doing to become part of the solution, instead of part of the problem!"

The technology of biomedicine is undergoing a revolution, and the cycles of change are accelerating steadily. For example, the Human Genome Project is beginning to provide information that we previously could only dream about. It and other research will allow us to gain understanding of how the body works beyond the cellular level to the level of molecules.

But technology is not enough. The incredible advances of the past century and in this first decade of the new millennium have saved and extended many lives. Sadly, they have produced limited effects on the general health of our population.

Moreover, many technological advances have been offset – even canceled out – by behavioral changes in society. While the human lifespan has been expanded dramatically, too many of the additional years are being spent in disability, pain and misery, as degenerative disease becomes a standard condition of our later years.

Chronic health conditions exist in every corner of the industrialized world. There is no Shangri-la or safe haven. What we used to think were conditions of the elderly or unfortunate circumstances of a small segment of society have become part of every neighborhood, every family, every home, and every age group.

Each of us knows someone whose life has been influenced and shaped by a chronic condition: a family with a child who is developmentally or physically challenged; a relative with Alzheimer's or Parkinson's disease; a grandmother or aunt with osteoporosis; an associate battling cancer; a cousin needing daily insulin injections because of adult-onset diabetes; an acquaintance confined to a wheelchair as a result of a stroke; and an overweight, sedentary neighbor with the beginning signs of heart disease.

Most of these individuals I am describing are not in nursing homes or extended care facilities. They are living among us. They *are* us. And they are the previews of a future documentary about our children.

Often, I am tempted to ask the general audiences I speak to: "How many of you in this room plan to spend your final, golden years in a nursing home or long-term health facility, unable to care for yourselves?"

I doubt that anyone would raise his or her hand. And, yet, the statistics are shockingly clear. By 2030, it is projected, nearly 150 million Americans will have chronic degenerative disease and 42 million of those will be limited in their ability to go to school, to work, or to live independently.[2]

Even if you are fortunate enough not to become one of these statistics, one in four Americans currently provides some level of care for a person who has a chronic condition, with three out of four caregivers being women whose average age is 57. They are the "sandwich generation," simultaneously caring for children and for their own parents or elderly relatives.[3]

We need to look at the big picture. We need global perspective. Success in our culture is usually associated with material wealth. The images of shaded estates, luxury cars, and travel to exotic destinations bombard our senses. And herein lies a confusing paradox. We want immediate sensual gratification and, at the same time, we are desperate for eternal youth. Unless and until we get a reality check about the cause-and-effect principles involved, we are not going to view our lives as successful.

About 95 percent of the human beings on earth are poor, most of them desperately poor. Success to almost any member of such a family is to have some land to till, any job that pays, and a way to earn enough to provide the minimum, basic nourishment for their children to survive into adulthood.

We need to redefine success as learning as much, loving as much, sharing as much, and enjoying life as much, and for as long as we possibly can.

Of all the wisdom I have gained, the most important is the knowledge that health and time are two precious assets that we rarely recognize or appreciate until they have been depleted. As with time, health is the raw material of life. You can use it wisely or waste it or even kill it.

To accomplish all we are capable of, we would need a hundred lifetimes. If we had forever in our mortal lives, we would have no need to be concerned about our health, adjust our lifestyle habits, set goals, plan effectively, or set priorities. We could squander our time and health and perhaps still manage to realize our dreams, if only by chance. Yet in reality, we're given only one lifespan on earth to do our best.

Each human being now living has exactly 168 hours per week. Scientists can't invent new minutes, and even the super rich can't buy more hours. Queen Elizabeth I of England, the richest, most powerful woman on earth in her era, whispered these final words on her deathbed: "All my possessions for a moment of time!"

Even though we all are aware of the tradeoffs of quality time versus quantity time in our relationships, we are not used to thinking specifically about how our decisions cost us other opportunities. You may have heard the story of the circus juggler applied to each of us as we try to balance our priorities. I have heard the story repeated by speakers at conventions and by other writers, but have never been able to trace the identity of the original author:

When the circus juggler drops a ball, he lets it bounce, picking it up on the next bounce without losing his rhythm or concentration. He keeps right on juggling.

Many times we do the same thing. We lose our jobs but get another one on the first or second bounce. We may drop the ball on a sale, on an opportunity to move ahead, or in a business arrangement, and we either pick it up on the rebound or get a new one thrown in to replace what we just dropped.

But there's a critical difference between us and the circus juggler. Some of the balls or priorities we juggle just don't bounce. The more urgent priorities associated with deadlines and workloads have more elasticity than precious, delicate relationships, which are as fragile as fine crystal.

Balance involves distinguishing between the priorities that can bounce from the ones labeled "loved ones" and "health," which may shatter if we drop them.[4]

Handle your health priorities and those of your loved ones with care. They don't automatically bounce back!

We've often heard that 'youth is wasted on the young.' When it comes to our present-day society, this saying may be interpreted to mean that good health is wasted while we're young.

I have a vision of true health, where the people in the world can live in harmony, free from pain and suffering. World leadership used to center around power and being number one. It has often meant standing victoriously over a fallen adversary or competitor. As we move through the first decade of a new century, however, it is obvious that this must change. The world now has too many people, too few resources, and too delicate a balance between nature and technology for nations or individuals to operate in isolation. The leaders of the present and the future should be champions of cooperation more often than of competition.

The philosophy of the survival of the fittest, or the mentality of the law of the jungle, must give way to survival of the wisest and a philosophy of understanding, cooperation, knowledge and reason. Real leaders will get what they want by helping others get what *they* want. Interdependence will replace independence.

We will have no lasting peace on earth until there's a piece of pie in every mouth. The expectation of tomorrow's bigger, better pie, of which everyone will enjoy a larger piece, is what prevents people from struggling to the end over the division of today's pie. As students of the art of self-leadership, we must acknowledge that we are a vital but single unit of the larger body of the world's population. One group of human beings can no longer succeed – or, perhaps, even survive – without the others.

In the end, most of us discover that what others really care about is a shared vision, not a selfish vision. For a vision to be inspiring and worth sharing, it needs to bring out the best in all of us, not pander to the superficial and hedonistic urges in us. To gain the respect of others, we must first earn it. We must be respectable and respectful. To be a role model, we must first set a positive example worth emulating. To lead others, we first must lead ourselves.

We must look in the mirror when we ask who is responsible for our health and well-being. Each of us must become a life-long learner and leader in our family and among our peers.

Look into the mirror with me and reflect on the vast potential within you. Challenge your timeworn prejudices and assumptions about disease and cure, and replace them with knowledge about health and prevention.

One key to achieving optimal health is supporting a healthy metabolism. How do we do this? It is very much like building a house. An important consideration is quality construction material to withstand external environmental conditions. In building optimal health, the construction materials are nutrients – both macronutrients (the carbohydrates, proteins, and fats we eat), and micronutrients (vitamins, minerals, antioxidants, and trace elements). As I will discuss in the pages that follow, scientific studies over the past several decades have proven that our food, today, has diminished nutrient levels because of overprocessing and the exhaustion of nutrients in our farmland.

If the nutrients are not in the soil, they are not in our food. If overprocessing and adding preservatives to this food removes most of the remaining nutrients from our daily diets, then the nutrients cannot get into our bodies. It is no longer possible to receive all the nutrients we need by consuming even a very good diet. Intelligent cellular nutrition requires more knowledge and effort on our part to ensure that we at least get base amounts of all the essential nutrients.

Increasing this kind of awareness is what I hope to accomplish in this book. Another is to identify the enormous problems – in our environment, in our lifestyle choices, and in the way we approach health care – that we face in gaining and regaining true health in our advanced, industrialized societies. We also face the major challenge of helping other nations learn from our experience – so that they, too, can live longer in health, rather than longer in illness.

We need to believe and embrace the idea that true wealth and true health are synonymous. It is not what we have that counts. It is what we are able to continue to achieve and enjoy with what we have, and it is also the lessons we share with future generations. Life is a process, not a status.

Although it has been said that time is money, in truth, time is much more precious than money. Money spent or lost can be earned again. Time spent is gone forever and is directly related to the quality of your health.

Share my vision for a healthier future for you, your family, and everyone you meet so that you can enjoy the time of your lives to the fullest. Look inside with me through a microscope to the galaxy of life at the cellular level, and discover the possibilities I see when I speak of true health.

Chapter 2
The Toxic Cradle

"We live too short and die too long!"

When people hear me make that ominous declaration, they appear puzzled or shocked or both.

How can this be? they wonder. Aren't we actually living longer than any other generation before us? Doesn't modern medicine promise to extend our lives even further through scientific advances and technological breakthroughs? The answer to both of these questions is affirmative.

What, then, do I mean when I say, "We live too short and die too long?" Simply stated, we – in the wealthiest, industrialized societies – are living longer in poor health than ever before. Our quantity of life is increasing while our quality of life is decreasing, in spite of our ever-rising standard of living.

The degenerative diseases rampant in our aging populations

have caused a catastrophic crisis in our health-care delivery system, with little relief in sight. The term *chronic* has its roots in the ancient Greek word *chronos*, meaning "time," with chronic implying long-lasting conditions.

In Chapter 1, I briefly touched the tip of the iceberg, with statistics showing that by the year 2030 nearly 150 million Americans will have at least one chronic health condition.

What I didn't mention were the costs. By 2030, unless new systems of care are created and new lifestyle choices internalized by our people, chronic care alone will cost the United States nearly $800 billion annually in direct medical and nursing home costs.[5] No government will ever be able to finance that kind of growth in expenditures, let alone the hundreds of billions of dollars a year in lost productivity.

That is nearly double the expenditure of only a decade ago, and ten times the amount devoted to education and research. Chronic care costs make up the largest share of health-care dollars spent in the United States, or almost 70 percent of the total – and there is no end in sight.

The dilemma we face is expressed in the opening lines of Charles Dickens's classic book *A Tale of Two Cities*: "It was the best of times. It was the worst of times."

It is the worst of times because we live in an overpopulated, polluted, stress-inducing, dangerous world. It is the best of times because we have unparalleled access to knowledge that can help us conquer poverty and disease – if we can educate ourselves and our families to make the right choices and change our lifestyles accordingly.

We in the industrialized nations are no longer dying from the same diseases we did in previous generations. Infectious diseases such as influenza, pneumonia, tuberculosis, smallpox, diphtheria, and polio felled our ancestors until the early decades of the twentieth century. Now, with the exceptions of AIDS, tuberculosis, and pneumonia, contemporary Americans rarely die from infectious diseases.

Scientific advances in sanitation, diagnosis, treatment, prevention, and some pharmaceutical products, such as insulin, have enabled people to live longer with disabling injuries and chronic conditions. This paradoxical problem has been labeled the *Failure of Success*[6] because, during the past several decades, rapid increases in life expectancy from birth have been accompanied by an increase in the portion of that life spent in declining health. We have been successful in lengthening the quantity of life while failing to maintain the quality.

To the credit of scientists and health-care and health-education practitioners, the fastest growing group of elderly people in America is that segment over 85 years of age. Yet, this population is also the most vulnerable to chronic conditions. In addition, the "baby boomer" generation will soon enlarge the over-65 population to record levels, with a corresponding rise in the need for chronic care.

This chapter is prophetically titled, "The Toxic Cradle." But aren't we discussing chronic care in an aging population? No, we are not. Contrary to popular perceptions, the elderly represent fewer than one-third of those who have chronic conditions that cause limitations and disabilities.

Of those Americans needing help with either personal care

or home management of health conditions, more than 40 percent are under age 65. One in ten young adults and one in fifteen children have activity-limiting chronic conditions.[7] And those numbers are rising steadily. We are not only living longer in ill health, but are experiencing chronic health problems much earlier.

Ironically, we have replaced the infectious diseases that killed our ancestors with degenerative diseases that are largely man-made. By our own assault on the environment, as we have exploited our natural resources, and as a result of our lifestyle choices in a highly industrialized, wealthy society, we and our children are paying a terrible price for our material success:

• By damaging the ozone layer, we are more vulnerable to excessive, harmful ultraviolet rays and radiation from the sun

• By filling the air with poisonous fumes, we are choking our vital oxygen supply

• By polluting our oceans, rivers, and lakes, we are ruining our precious water sources

• By depositing harmful chemicals in our soil, we are damaging our food supply

We have poisoned our nest and developed toxic lifestyle habits that have given rise to a whole host of diseases largely unknown a century ago.

The number-one cause of death is cardiovascular disease, including heart attacks and stroke. Nearly 42 percent of all deaths in the U.S., or more than 1 million per year, are the result of cardiovascular disease.

Cancer is second, with over 23 percent of deaths, or some half a million per year, and there are more than 1 million new cases of cancer reported every year.

Diabetes now accounts for 28 percent of all new serious kidney disease and is a primary cause of adult blindness and non-trauma-related limb amputation. More than 15 million Americans suffer from diabetes, and tens of millions exhibit pre-clinical symptoms, most without any knowledge of their vulnerability. [8]

More than 25 million Americans, most of them women, suffer from osteoporosis, and arthritis afflicts more than 30 million men and women. As I mentioned earlier, we all know someone in our extended family, or that of a friend, living with the devastating effects of Alzheimer's or Parkinson's disease.

Asthma has reached epidemic proportions, and increasing incidences of a host of autoimmune diseases grow silently through the years, unnoticed, and then announce their presence as full-blown, often incurable illnesses, which dims our hopes for enjoying the years we have worked and waited for, for so long.

Scientific research in the past decade has provided irrefutable evidence that one of the two primary causes of degenerative disease is oxidative damage. Oxidative damage is a term that refers to the harm caused to the cells of our bodies as a result of free-radical activity. Oxygen, which is critical to sustain human life, turns out to be a double-edged sword.

A free radical is any molecule, often of oxygen, that has unpaired electrons. Such molecules are very reactive and unstable. Stable atoms or molecules always have electrons in pairs to balance their nuclear forces. Having lost one of its paired electrons, a molecule becomes unbalanced, and a free radical is formed. This sets up a chain reaction in neighboring molecules, with free radicals pulling electrons out of the nearest stable molecules of any material they touch.

Upon losing an electron, each molecule affected by a free radical then becomes a new free radical, and thus the destructive chain reaction continues. Free radicals steal electrons from molecules in the cell's membranes, lipids, proteins, enzymes, or DNA and, in the process, damage the cellular structures within every tissue of our bodies.

Free radicals are generated by our polluted environment, and they are also by-products of our own cellular metabolism. Their presence in biological systems was first identified by scientists in the early 1960s.[9] In certain disease states, or when we are experiencing emotional or physical stress – such as high-intensity exercise – our metabolic rate increases and we generate even more free radicals into our system.

Our bodies have their own marvelous defense systems against oxidation caused by free radicals. Internally, we create endogenous antioxidants within our cells, including enzymes, coenzymes, and sulfur-containing molecules such as glutathione. These naturally occurring antioxidants donate an electron to the free radical, rendering it harmless. These natural antioxidants provide some protection, but are woefully inadequate to provide a full defense against oxidative damage in the toxic cradle of our present-day environment of free radicals.

Our next major line of defense consists of exogenous antioxidants obtained through the food we eat. These dietary antioxidants include certain vitamins and an assortment of bioflavonoids extracted from fruits and vegetables. There are also a number of minerals that, while not antioxidants themselves, interact synergistically with our internal antioxidant regenerating systems to provide more effective protection against free-radical damage.

I will cover the body's incredible ability to heal itself – if it receives the right nutrients in the correct amounts and ratios – in a later chapter. This discussion presents the daunting problems we face and gives you an awareness of the consequences. It is my fervent hope that this information will spur you into a lifestyle decision that will benefit you, your children, and the generations that will follow.

Children Become What They See

Yes, we are nurtured in a toxic cradle. Cardiovascular disease begins in childhood. Dietary and lifestyle habits in our early years establish long-term outcomes. Factors including poor dietary habits, lack of physical exercise, adolescent obesity, and smoking have been linked to heart disease and other degenerative diseases.

We are overfed and undernourished. In a time-starved world, we also are becoming a nutrition-starved society. The lure of fast foods has become a daily diet of harmful foods.

The shocking evidence of what this means to our present and future generations is illustrated in research that has discovered atherosclerosis in children two to fifteen years of age. One study found that the disease affects approximately 30 percent of adolescents between the ages of 16 to 20 years, 50 percent of young adults between 21 and 25, and 75 percent of adults 26 to 39.[10]

The unimaginable is occurring: heart disease in primary and secondary school children.

A cycle of continuing susceptibility to degenerative disease is set up when young people adopt the poor lifestyle habits of their adult role models and become that to which they are exposed. Watching thousands of hours of television each year, children are subject to seductive advertising linking snack foods and drive-through pit stops with celebrities and the good life. Conventional wisdom about healthy meals has been replaced by the word *convenience* and useful information on nutrition is almost non-existent.

There can be no question that diet plays a central role in determining the risks of many birth defects, childhood illnesses, and chronic degenerative diseases. Increasing numbers of Americans are overweight, including children. Nearly one-third of our daily energy intake comes through consumption of such calorie-rich, nutrient-poor snack foods as candy, soft drinks, alcoholic beverages, chips, and cookies. Only one-quarter of children and adults achieve even minimal recommendations for fruit and vegetable intake. Not surprisingly, nearly one-quarter of all vegetables consumed by children and adolescents are greasy french fries.[11]

Moreover, families are increasingly being exposed to a toxic environment and – lacking optimal nutrition – are unable to effectively battle the oxidative damage resulting from higher levels of free radicals. Tragically, our children are at the highest risk.

Children are more vulnerable to toxic substances than adults, in part simply because they are more exposed. Pound for pound of body weight, children drink more water, and eat more food than adults. In addition, their behavior patterns, such as playing close to the ground and, engaging in hand-to-mouth activities, can increase their exposure to potential toxins in the environment.

Every day the average adult breathes over 3,000 gallons of air, and children breathe even more air per pound of body weight. The large volume of air passing in and over the delicate membranes of the airways and lungs each week, month, and year, gradually deposits airborne lead, hydrocarbons and soot in dangerous amounts.

When you hear a child coughing at play, it's likely that the protective cilia lining the airways are full of pollutants, and the natural reflex of coughing is the body's way of bringing the toxic substances – along with epithelial cells – up and out.[12]

Polluted air is only one of the health threats for children today. In the last 50 years, more than 75,000 chemicals have been developed and introduced into the environment. Meanwhile, the overall incidence of childhood cancer increased 10 percent over the last 20 years.[13]

The most common form of cancer in children is leukemia, and the incidence of childhood leukemia rose about 1 percent every year from 1977 to 1995. Improved treatments have reduced deaths from this disease, but we still don't know the definitive cause. However, the factors most closely associated with leukemia risk are ionizing radiation, pesticides, solvents, electric and magnetic fields, and radon exposure – all factors that we can control, if we choose.

What I have outlined so far is the uphill battle we face in gaining true health in this millennium. We can no longer wait for disease to arrive at our homes as a full-blown, life-threatening event and then hope and pray for a cure. We cannot tolerate a toxic cradle of pollution and, at the same time, provide our children with only 1 percent of the dietary basics they need to help fight free-radical damage.

The answers, I believe, lie in a new awareness about life at the cellular level. I referred to each living cell in our bodies as the fundamental unit of life. Poison it, injure it, or starve it, and the resulting damage causes disease and degeneration. Nurture it, protect it, and feed it with the nutrients it needs, and it repairs itself, providing health and longevity.

We are at the crossroads of an unprecedented shift in lifestyles that will alter the future of humankind. The real paradox is that the wealthiest nations are among the unhealthiest nations in the world.

Rather than take the easy, low road to convenience, let us take the high road to long-term health. The easy way is to sell your health to the merchandisers of unhealthy, processed foods. The right way is to take the road less traveled, the road to optimal nutrition. This is the journey I have undertaken, and I believe it will ultimately be the road best traveled for you.

Chapter 3
The Road Best Traveled

In our journey toward fulfillment, we must remember that success is a process, not a destination, let alone a summit. Destinations inevitably involve arrivals and endings.

Life can be likened to an endless range of mountains, with peaks and valleys, inclines and descents, and always more peaks ahead to climb. You and I each climb the "Mount Everest" in our lives, as Sir Edmund Hillary did his, "because it's there" and also for the sheer exhilaration of testing our knowledge, skill, and courage.

For myself, I've always felt the word *retired* was misspelled. The word should be *retried* or, perhaps, *reinspired. Retired* implies a concluded career or could mean tired again, or tired for the final time. A commencement ceremony after one career or major achievement should bring the anticipation of another peak experience ahead, challenging and enriching our bodies, minds, and souls in new, creative pursuits, different from any we may have experienced or imagined before.

The idea of arriving at a permanent plateau called success is a myth. I can have successful moments in certain arenas at certain times. Next week I may not fare as well. The market may go down. A medical diagnosis can cause concerns. A member of the family can be in need. To say "I am a success" is to attach some kind of permanence to the word, as if nothing will ever change, as if things will always be the way they are now.

But things don't stay the same. Everything changes – above all the meaning of success. My main purpose is to encourage you to become an agent for positive change in your lifestyle and health choices, rather than become a victim of change.

Screen actor and director, Robert Redford, lives and works as a film institute producer and environmentalist at his Sundance center in the mountains near the USANA Health Sciences corporate headquarters in Utah. Years ago, when he was named the top motion picture box office drawing card in America, he told a TV interviewer that, while his ambition had always been to reach the top, he believed that to achieve that goal he had to avoid being seduced by fame. Whenever he was tempted to believe his own publicity, he reminded himself that success is something to spar with, but never to embrace. Success is fickle and fleeting, but living successfully by being the best we can be is always within our power.

My own upbringing and experience have confirmed that success is a way of traveling. The title of this chapter, "The Road Best Traveled," was inspired by "The Road Not Taken," a well-known work by Robert Frost, former American poet laureate. Which road is best? Frost said the road less traveled made all the difference.

Certainly all roads don't lead to Napoleon, North Dakota, where my parents and then my brothers and I were raised. You could definitely say that the road to our town fit the description "road less traveled." It is located between two road signs. One reads "Reduced Speed Ahead" and the other, not far away, reads "Resume Speed."

That is just a tongue-in-cheek way of admitting that you don't have to go through Napoleon – population about 1,000 – to get to any major city. To be accurate, which is an idiosyncrasy of mine, I was born in 1940 in a hospital in the big city of Bismarck, population about 20,000. I was the first member of my family not to be born at home. My adventure in the big city of Bismarck lasted all of three days, before I returned home from the hospital to start my journey.

I am the youngest of three brothers. My father, Adam, and mother, Bertha, were of German heritage. They spent their lives in the environs of Napoleon, having a total of 12 brothers and sisters in each of their own families.

Our ancestors left Germany and settled in southern Russia when Catherine the Great was encouraging German farmers to move to that part of her empire now known as the Ukraine. These hard-working, God-abiding, closely knit families preserved their German culture, including language and food, throughout their sojourn in Russia and after they emigrated to the United States. I remember well the German dialect my grandparents spoke when I was a child.

Forced to abandon their farms by the rising threat of Russian nationalism at the end of the nineteenth century, they left their rural enclaves by train and then came by ship to the U.S., settling in North Dakota. At the time I was writing this book, I made a trip to the Ukraine in the hope of learning more about my family's roots.

As part of the ongoing philanthropic support of the company I founded, USANA Health Sciences, for the Children's Hunger Fund, I had been visiting orphanages in Romania and the Ukraine that have been receiving financial aid and nutritional supplements from us to enhance the health of thousands of castaway children. It was a heart-wrenching, sobering experience that could be the subject of a future book.

One morning we were driving in an area about 100 kilometers north of Odessa, not far from the area where my ancestors had lived. I couldn't help smiling knowingly as we drove through miles of starkly beautiful, rolling fields of grain. If I had ever wondered why my relatives left the Ukraine and settled in Napoleon, North Dakota, I would wonder no more. Not only is the terrain remarkably identical, but the latitudes of the two areas, though worlds apart, are virtually the same. Driving through that area of the Ukraine is like driving on the road less traveled near my hometown in North Dakota.

Although my ancestors brought very little Russian influence to America, I confess to having a special feeling for the Russian people, a feeling that has motivated me to fund medical research in Moscow and to engage several outstanding Russian scientists to further our nutritional work at USANA Health Sciences.

Recently, we have collaborated with the scientists at the Cardiology Research Institute in Moscow in cytotoxicity studies of oxidized lipids (fats). We were able to spin down blood samples using the institute's ultracentrifuges and isolate the chylomicron fractions that presumably contained the consumed oxidized lipids. Then we introduced them into cell cultures to see how the cells reacted to the ingested lipids. The results were amazing. We saw significant cell damage after the application of chylomicron fractions. As importantly, we were able to show that the damage was minimized when certain antioxidants were also fed to the human volunteers.

As an analogy, let's say you ate a typical fast-food selection of burgers, fries, and a chocolate shake, and we took blood samples immediately afterward, using the procedures just outlined. Were we to isolate the fractions that contain the oxidized fat from that meal, you would be shocked by the results. You would see with your own eyes the cell damage that has taken place. I have shown slides of this experiment in public lectures, and the audiences have looked carefully at the luncheon menus on that day from a more educated perspective.

Fortunately, with the right nutrition and lifestyle we can reduce that kind of damage. It is more effective to prevent a fire than to engage in fire-fighting measures to stop the damage.

It is sadly ironic that good nutritional products are needed desperately by the hungry, undernourished children in the villages and orphanages of Latin America and Eastern Europe and also by the overfed, but otherwise well-cared-for, children in our abundant America.

I guess I'm getting ahead of myself. After all, I'm still a young boy in North Dakota at this point in the story.

My boyhood in Napoleon was happy as far as I can

remember, though not exceptional. I wasn't a star athlete, yet I enjoyed sports and lettered in all the major high school sports. I loved music, sang in the choir and played in the band. I would have preferred to master the violin, but my older brother had a trumpet. At my mother's insistence and, as a result of her frugal practicality, I played in the brass section for the remainder of my musical career.

My mother was a very religious person. She made certain that we went to church every Sunday, as well as church camps every summer. It was her hope that I would become a minister. I think she was disappointed, at first, with my passion for the life sciences and music as possible career choices.

It was a comfortable life in a loving home with good examples to follow. Like the generations before ours and like almost everyone else in that area of North Dakota in those days, my father was a farmer. As we did our chores, I recall that the soil was rich with mineral deposits and those nutrients ended up in the food that was on our dinner table.

Unlike most of his contemporaries, my dad, Adam, also was a businessman. He wasn't content just to farm. He and a younger brother started a hardware store, a furniture store, then bought a John Deere farm implement shop and a Ford dealership. I'm sure that some of my entrepreneurial spirit emanated from his example.

Because of these businesses, my parents moved from their farm to a home in town. They were considered "sidewalk farmers" because they lived in town and farmed outside of town. We ate well, but were not wealthy – we had what you would call a modest life.

There were several events during my high school years that could be described as life forming. One was my introduction to the work of Linus Pauling, which I eagerly studied and wrote term papers about in my science classes.

In my opinion, Linus Pauling – a genius and a maverick – was arguably the most brilliant scientist ever produced by the United States. He is the only individual to have been awarded two unshared Nobel Prizes. It is difficult to overestimate the profound effect Dr. Pauling's thinking about the nature of the universe – his scientific and humanitarian view of the world – has had on all of us. His influence on me was incalculable.

One most important insight I gained from him was how a tiny change – a single base-pair error at the molecular level – could be the cause of serious disease. His work on sickle-cell anemia remains a landmark example of scientific investigation in the annals of medicine. I'll always remember his discovery about the hazards of radioactivity and the fact that the negative effects of radioactive exposure are cumulative over one's lifetime.

That he was a chemist who made significant contributions beyond his own primary educational discipline also helped shape my future outlook. Here was a Nobel laureate as at home with research on the terrible consequences of nuclear war as he was with his breakthrough studies on the positive benefits of vitamin C as a preventive therapy. He planted the first seeds that led to serious investigation of nutrition as therapy for degenerative diseases.

From Linus Pauling's example, I learned to persist when I believed I was correct, despite the criticisms of others – especially those in positions of authority. Dr. Pauling had achieved much and thus had much to risk by challenging the establishment. I didn't necessarily start my college education as a complete idealist, but I knew I wanted to act on my own convictions, rather than go along with the crowd on the road most traveled.

Another special kinship I felt with Linus Pauling was that his father died at the age of 33, when Linus was only nine years old. My father died when I was 17.

My father was highly regarded as a man of generosity and compassion. Years later, when I was coming home from college and would stop by a farm or store in our area, all I had to do was mention that I was Adam Wentz's son, and they would roll out the red carpet for me. It seemed that everybody I met had been a recipient of my father's help or generosity, or that they simply had a great deal of admiration and respect for him.

That made it even harder to have lost him at such a young age. He died at 57 from heart disease, which he had lived with as far back as I can remember, having spent time in hospitals and long-term care facilities. It was a very traumatic experience because I wanted his approval so much; and yet, like other teenagers, I felt I hadn't taken enough time for him. When he was gone, of course, it was too late. I believe that some of my drive to contribute to society can be attributed to a desire to compensate for his loss and to be worthy of his respect, as he was respected by others.

Pondering my future, I left home after graduation from high school to attend North Central College in Naperville, Illinois. In considering colleges, I had learned that North Central had strong academic programs in pre-med and music, two of my major interests. Just as it would be difficult to ride two horses at the same time, I found it equally challenging to consider a double major in music and biology.

I remember my biology professor admonishing me after I earned a low grade in organic chemistry: "Myron, if you're going to be successful in the medical sciences, you're going to have to focus on those subjects. It's your choice." It was not an easy decision to put my love of music in the background, but I made what I felt was the right choice and earned a bachelor's degree in biology and pre-med in 1963.

I will never regret that decision – and, at the same time, I have never ended my love affair with beautiful music of every type, though I have a special fondness for opera and classical music. One of my favorite present-day diversions is to sit on the deck of my yacht, *La Vie*, in a remote, crystal-clear bay off the British Virgin Islands and turn up the volume on the stereo to reach the heavens with the rich sounds of Luciano Pavarotti.

Reading Pavarotti's biography, I found that his father encouraged him to become a professional singer, while his mother thought he should pursue the more secure profession of teaching. Wanting to please both his parents, he devoted himself to both fields. He took singing lessons while growing up in Modena, Italy, and enrolled in a teachers' college at the same time.

Upon graduation, he approached his father for career counseling: "Father, shall I be a teacher or a singer?" "Luciano," his father said, "if you try to sit in two chairs, you will fall between them. In life, *you* must choose one chair."[14]

I don't presume to imply that I could have had a successful career in music had that been my choice. As it has turned out, I have the best of both worlds. I can listen with abandon to the best of all the great music while studying the latest proceedings concerning molecular nutrition in stacks of scientific publications. It's a win-win proposition.

Most of my fellow students who pursued life science studies at North Central College went on to medical school. It was the thing to do. But, I guess I'm not a me-too person. I decided to carve out a different kind of career that I thought would be more creative and engaging. Rather than going the route of being a dispenser of drugs and a front-office medical practitioner, I wanted to create the scientific solutions to the needs of mankind – to develop and provide the tools for medicine, rather than just employ them.

Armed with some basic education in the life sciences and a zest for finding the area in which the greater contribution to health lay, I accepted a position as the microbiologist for the state health department. While I thought the availability of the job was circumstance, it was soon obvious that the opportunity was no accident. During that time it became clear that I would pursue the study of infectious diseases.

Those were society's biggest health challenges – I wanted to meet them. Scientific journals were full of theories, research, and discoveries involving infectious diseases. Even the general public seemed tuned-in, as evidenced by a best-selling book at the time, "Microbe Hunters," by Paul de Kruif. I enrolled in graduate school in medical microbiology at the University of North Dakota, while continuing my job at the health department, and earned a master's degree in microbiology.

Leaving North Dakota, I headed for the University of Utah in Salt Lake City to pursue a Ph.D. I was fascinated with the science of the body's ability to respond to infectious disease, and this school boasted one of the strongest immunology departments, with an impressive faculty.

Reflecting on my early beginnings, from the prairie of Napoleon to the mountains of Salt Lake City, one memory stands out as a defining moment. When I announced to my mother my intention to go into medical science, she looked at me and said softly, "I wish you had been born earlier, so you could have done something to allow your father to live longer." Her words left an indelible imprint that became one of the catalysts for my dedication to do what I could do to help others.

If the road less traveled is the road you've chosen – never mind whether you're racing ahead, struggling on an upgrade, or resting a moment while you catch your breath – you know that life is not a book that is finished when you've read its last pages. You know that it's more like the vast mountain ranges, prairies, and rolling valleys of farmland, whether you're traveling in the Russian Ukraine, the out-skirts of Napoleon, North Dakota, or the Wasatch Range in Utah.

You know life is a growing field that changes with the seasons. It grows well in the summer and less well in the fall. What you planted in the spring might die in the winter. But when you plant again, tending the soil and watering the seeds, you will reap again.

You also know that it's not necessary to invite weeds and intruders into your garden. They move right in anyway, and in great numbers. No planting is necessary, but getting your garden to produce food for family, friends, and those in need takes constant attention and vigilance. A shared vision is always more enriching than a selfish one. It also inspires more commitment and dedication.

During many periods of history, farmers left a corner of their crops unharvested so that the less fortunate might use them for food. This practice ensured that everyone had enough to eat and also demonstrated the farmers' compassion. It showed that they cared about others and didn't need to have it all in order to feel successful.

It was what one did on the road best traveled.

Chapter 4
Diagnosing Infectious Disease

There was a time when a career as a scientist was, in itself, a noble and life-consuming goal. Basic research involves studies with no specific intent to solve particular problems or with immediate benefits to society. Applied research is directed toward achieving specific results that will affect the well-being of people.

Although I had decided not to become a front-office health practitioner, I was motivated to create and develop tools that could be used by health-care professionals in dealing with the scourge of infectious diseases present in our society. In the years immediately following my doctoral studies at the University of Utah, I plunged into positions of increasing responsibility in microbiology laboratories at several medical clinics and hospitals in the midwestern United States.

I felt a turn in the road looming on the near horizon. In those years, you were expected to use the knowledge you had gained in graduate school to further scientific knowledge without concern for such mundane details as getting the benefits of your

40   *Invisible Miracles*

discoveries to people and to patients. Also, I was beginning to understand the degree of politics and bureaucracy inherent in the institutional scientific community.

To exacerbate my dilemma, science, especially medical science, was just beginning to proliferate into big business. I knew I did not want to be an employee of a pharmaceutical company, nor did I want to climb into the ivory tower of basic research or play king of the mountain in some institutional hierarchy. Thinking back to the influence of Linus Pauling, the maverick, and relying on entrepreneurial instincts inherited from my father, I took a fork in the road and struck out on my own.

There were only two viral diseases at that time – hepatitis and rubella – whose diagnoses could be confirmed in the laboratory. I decided to try my hand at developing badly needed tests for other viral infections. My hope was that such tests could be completed and results reported to physicians before the patients left the hospital – much more rapidly than was the standard practice.

I returned to Salt Lake City, Utah, where a fully equipped laboratory with cell culture capabilities stood vacant. The facilities had been used by The Salk Institute for Biological Studies, with headquarters in La Jolla, California. Dr. Jonas Salk, founder and developer of the first effective polio vaccine, had a particular interest in a rather obscure viral infection, Aleutian Disease, which commercially bred mink were subject to. These mink experiments did not prove fruitful for the Salk team, and their decision to terminate the project was a fortunate event for me.

I have great respect for Salk as a scientist and a man of vision. He felt that scientists suffer no failures, only unprofitable avenues to pursue. As a peer of Linus Pauling, Jonas Salk viewed biology as a science and as a basic cultural discipline revealing converging relationships between man and the physical universe – between man and the sciences, arts, religions, and humanistic values.

Salk, like Pauling, was not accepted by the establishment. He often commented that the worst tragedy that could have befallen him was his success, because of the criticism and envy it spawned within the establishment. He said he couldn't possibly have become a member of his own institute had he not founded it himself.

I sold everything I owned, got a loan from the Small Business Administration, and bought the equipment I needed to develop viral diagnostic assays. My one-man business came complete with a name and a small, ongoing laboratory services contract to keep the doors open. It involved electrophoresis for Aleutian Disease virus for the Fur Breeders Association. What the laboratory and mink farm failed to do for Salk was a blessing for me, although the aroma during a hot, valley inversion was barely tolerable.

Gull Laboratories was launched in September 1974, and by June 1977, only two and a half years later, several of my viral diagnostic assays were cleared by the U. S. Food and Drug Administration and were ready for marketing to clinical and hospital laboratories. I was spurred forward by the knowledge that the large pharmaceutical firms had been attempting for years, unsuccessfully, to do the same thing I was trying to do.

I knew if I was going to compete successfully, despite the huge disparity in financial resources – almost as a David against Goliath – I would have to have the most technologically advanced tests possible. I decided I would grow all the viruses known at that time to be of diagnostic importance to humans. With these cultures I could prepare test systems for the diseases these viruses caused, and that's what I did.

I decided to focus on the herpes viruses first and developed culture methods and assays for most of them. Those were the first such products on the market. The breakthrough test that firmly established the success of Gull Laboratories worldwide was the assay for the Epstein-Barr virus. The world – especially Europe – was waiting for that assay. Of the more than 30 diagnostic tests I developed, the Epstein-Barr virus assay was the one I became identified with in medical diagnostics. It was a test that could not be duplicated elsewhere, and to this day remains the gold standard for diagnosing an infection with that virus.

At that time, when a bacterial infection was diagnosed, the physician had an arsenal of antibiotics to use in eradicating the pathogen. Antiviral drugs, however, were only in the development stage in the 1970s and, as a result, many doctors left unsuspected viral infections undiagnosed. There was an alternative diagnostic test for the Epstein-Barr virus, the heterophile test, but it was not very specific and was useless in identifying infection in children.

There were two important reasons for testing for infection with EBV. First, atypical mononucleosis was important to diagnose because it signaled potential immunological abnormalities. The second reason was to obtain information that would permit ruling out the numerous disorders that an EBV infection could mimic. An infection with *Toxoplasma gondii*, for example, could be potentially dangerous for a woman in her first trimester of pregnancy.

With no advertising – indeed, virtually no marketing efforts at all – sales of the Gull Epstein-Barr tests grew steadily from month to month throughout the world.

It was a source of pride for me to have looked beyond the financial rewards that accompanied the success of Gull Laboratories to the understanding that here was a case of a previously unmet medical need being filled. Here were tools for health professionals that could immediately benefit patients.

One reason for my success in developing viral diagnostics was the quality of the cell culture operations at Gull Laboratories. Viruses cannot reproduce on their own, but must hijack the metabolic machinery of the host cell to manufacture the components, which then go into assembly of the viral particles. I knew that, to develop the best viral assays, I had to produce the best viral antigens. But since viruses need host cells to reproduce, I couldn't produce good viruses unless I could grow healthy, fully competent cells.

Cells in culture can be very troublesome. After months of vigorous growing they can suddenly die off without warning. They are very sensitive to their environment, especially to the nutrients in the culture medium. This can be illustrated by an anecdote about a cell culture laboratory that relocated from the East to the West coast. The cell cultures were almost all lost in the new laboratories because of a minor difference in the purity of the water supply. Water had to be transported cross-country by air for almost a year before the cells adapted to the new growing conditions.

Gull Laboratories had one of the finest cell culture facilities of the day. During my many years of hands-on work with the cultures, I had developed an exceptional training program and attracted and developed some of the industry's best cell-culture technologists. As is the case in all the sciences, intuition and common sense were valuable allies to the sophisticated equipment and technical know-how required for this specialized science within a science.

Among the secrets of our success at Gull was a comprehensive knowledge of the nutritional requirements of the different cell lines. With the right combination of all the nutrients essential for life, I could maintain cells in a healthy state almost indefinitely, without any signs of degeneration or disease.

What I didn't realize at the time was that this knowledge would bring about the revolutionary next stage in my scientific journey. The principles of good nutrition are universal. If we can supply nutrients to the human body in a comprehensive manner on a daily basis with the full spectrum of essential nutrients in the right forms, amounts, and in the proper balance, we can achieve long-term health.

Health, after all, begins at the cellular level.

Chapter 5
Cells: The Fundamental Units of Life

I remember when I was a high-school kid fascinated with biology, reading a description of the cell as a "bag of protoplasm." Our knowledge of the workings of the cell has changed a lot in the ensuing decades. For instance, we now know there is no such thing as protoplasm, and we know the cell is a whole lot more than just a passive bag. Every living cell in our bodies is a dynamic, fascinating world of its own; ever-changing yet of amazing stability; ever-new but based on chemical and electrical principles as old as life itself. To me, the cell is a bundle of miracles.

Cells and the Health of the Body

Our health depends on what happens within the many different types of cells that make up our bodies. Every disease begins in the individual cell, and that's where health is regained as well. The health of the cell depends, in turn, on the functions of millions of critical molecules inside each cell and on the thousands of tiny structures that the cell manufactures, maintains, and passes on to following generations.

The body can be compared to a community with the various organs and tissues each playing their separate roles, each of which benefits the whole organism. The nervous system provides communications similar to the telephone companies. The digestive system provides raw materials and fuel to the organs and tissues of the body, where new proteins are manufactured and fuel is burned for movement and other activities. If any individual organ declines in its ability to perform its function, the whole organism becomes dysfunctional and degenerates.

Each of the hundred trillion cells in our bodies is itself similar to another, more basic community, again with a multitude of separate structures called *organelles*, which perform a wide variety of specialized tasks. Each of the organelles must perform its function as needed by the cell, depending on the changing conditions, exactly as the organs of the body must all be healthy for the body itself to be healthy. Organelles provide the organization that allows plants and animals to have specialized cells and tissues required by large, complex organisms such as human beings.

If we look closely enough, to a dimension smaller even than the organelles, to the molecular level, we see that the cell is an extremely busy place. In the space of about one-tenth of a millimeter, some 20,000 different proteins are manufactured on a regular basis. Each of these proteins requires a half dozen or more steps for synthesis – totaling hundreds of thousands of reactions happening every moment – and the right amount and correct form of each substance must be directed to the place where it is needed, when it is needed.

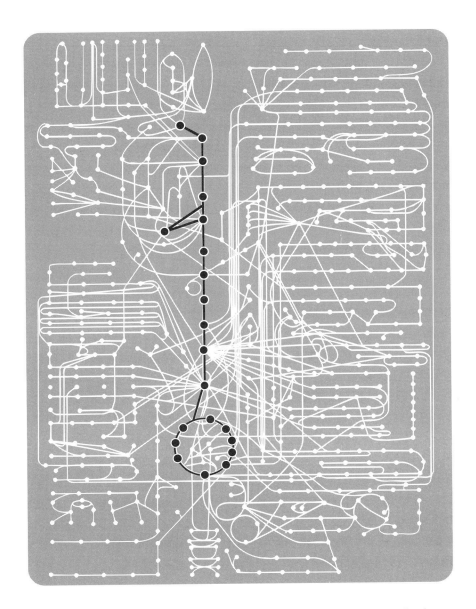

What seems like an impossibly complex maze is a simplified illustration of only some of the thousands of chemical reactions that may be occurring every moment in trillions of cells in the human body. Highlighted in the center are the glycolytic pathway and the Krebs cycle, the sequence of reactions that produces the cell's energy.
(Adapted from Alberts, et. al., Molecular Biology of the Cell, 1989.)

All of these reactions require energy input, which is obtained from the breakdown of sugars. In addition, the cell is constantly remodeling itself: lipids and proteins are metabolized and then modified for insertion into the cell membranes; carbohydrates are modified and stored as glycogen (starch).

Just as in the rest of nature, much of the substance of the cells is recycled and used again and again, especially the minerals. Each day about seven percent of the molecules of the body are "turned over" – disassembled from the structures they are part of and reassembled into new structures. That means most of the molecules in your body are turned over every two weeks!

This steady exchange of materials within the body provides flexibility in dealing with an ever-changing exterior environment. The key to health is to maintain stability in the midst of all this activity. Providing optimal nutrition for the cells to use in repairing and regenerating themselves is essential to keeping all of these activities on track.

The cell is a world of wonders and the subject of whole libraries of textbooks. Because this is not a textbook, but only an overview of how I've arrived at this point in my life, we'll look at only the major structures of the cell and take a very brief overview of the functions they perform (see cell illustration facing page 58).

The Nucleus

The nucleus, the best known of the cell's organelles, is the control center for all the activities of the cell. The information needed to perform all the cell's activities is encoded in the deoxyribonucleic acid (DNA) in the nucleus. The DNA is arranged in two spiraling strands wound around each other (the "double helix"). The sequence of nucleotide pairs with complementary shapes determines the so-called genetic code.

Surprisingly, more than 80 percent of the DNA in our genes is "junk" DNA, serving no known purpose. In the segments that are essential to us are more than 30,000 separate genes, each of which dictates the exact sequence of amino acids that make up the more than 20,000 different proteins manufactured by human cells. The timing of the production, as well as the amounts of each protein, is controlled by sensitive and complex feedback systems, some of them operating within the cell and others throughout the body.

Within the nucleus, the genetic material is in a loose arrangement with nuclear proteins most of the time, condensing to structures called chromosomes when the cell is preparing to reproduce. The nucleus is closely guarded by the nuclear envelope, a complex structure that consists of inner and outer membranes, an underlying nuclear lamina, and nuclear pore complexes. The membranes keep the nuclear material separate from the cytoplasm, but allow passage of small polar molecules and macromolecules, particularly RNAs. This "messenger RNA" may be thousands of bases in length and carries instructions for the assembly of proteins. Each time a cell reproduces itself, the membranes must be broken down and then reassembled in the two daughter cells.

The Life Cycle of a Cell

Cells that are actively reproducing follow a definite four-step program of cell growth, DNA replication, distribution of the duplicated chromosomes to the daughter cells and, finally, division into two new, individual cells. Each of these stages is easy to identify through the microscope in human cells in culture. Healthy cells in my tissue culture laboratories completed the cell cycle, including the birth of two daughter cells, approximately every 24 hours.

The cell cycle is regulated by both external and internal signals, including checkpoints ensuring that each of the daughter cells receives complete and functional genomes (the full component of genetic material). The detection of such problems as misaligned chromosomes, damaged DNA, or incompletely replicated DNA can bring the cycle to a halt. Inadequate nutrition can also result in a slowing or cessation of cell reproduction, both in the laboratory and in the body.

Cell Regeneration

The cells have amazing powers of regeneration, a capability that is essential to providing the body with the ability to function well over a lifetime. Depending on which organs they are part of, the cells in your body go through a cycle of generation, wear and tear, and replacement as often as every couple of days. The cells of some organs are regenerated frequently and, for each replication the DNA must be copied perfectly.

We know that blood cells turn over rapidly, and the epithelial cells lining the intestine are continually replacing older cells. An incredible 17 billion epithelial cells are replaced every day in this process, and the entire surface of the small intestine is replaced every five days.

We completely change our skin approximately every 27 days, which amounts to almost a thousand new skins in a lifetime.

We shed about 600,000 flakes of skin each hour, which adds up to 1.5 pounds each year. By 70 years of age, we will have lost 105 pounds (48 kilograms) of skin – equal to about two-thirds of our adult body weight (thank goodness for vacuum cleaners!).

Meanwhile, on the inside, our bones undergo a constant dismantling and remodeling, a process that slows only in the elderly. In fact, the skeleton is renewed every two years, with the bones sustaining the most daily wear and tear demonstrating the highest rate of renewal and replacement.

Some organs suffer significant injury in the course of performing their normal functions, and large numbers of their cells must be replaced. Perhaps the best example is the liver. In addition to manufacturing vital metabolic substances such as cholesterol and clotting proteins, liver cells detoxify the body of such harmful chemicals as drugs and alcohol. This detoxification process can cause severe damage to the cells as they sacrifice themselves to protect the body. It's not just coincidence that the liver is our only internal organ able to regenerate large parts of itself.

DNA Packing

Every cell carries all the DNA needed to be any kind of human cell, even though only a small fraction of it may be used by any single type of cell. The DNA content of each cell is an amazing example of efficient packaging. In the bacterium *Escherichia coli (E. coli)*, a DNA molecule of about 1,300 micrometers in length must fit inside a cell that is about 1 micrometer in diameter and 2 micrometers in length. That's the equivalent of packing about 18 meters (60 feet) of sewing thread into a thimble.

This is even more of a problem for human cells, which contain a thousand times as much DNA as *E. coli* does. To accomplish this, the cells wind the DNA strands around cores of protein (histone) and then into supercoils. The largest cell in the human body is the egg, produced by the ovaries of the female; it is smaller than the dot at the end of this sentence. If the DNA of all the chromosomes in this cell, or in almost any of the other cells in the body, was stretched out in a single line, it would extend for two meters, about six feet.

To extend our analogy of packing a piece of thread into a space equivalent to the size of a thimble, we would have to compress a 10-mile-long thread into a box that is one foot square, a 50,000-fold reduction. Connecting *all* the DNA in *all* the 100 trillion cells in your body in one line could reach all the way to the moon and back.

DNA Repair

With a total of three billion pairs of nucleotides in each cell, there are millions of opportunities for copying errors during the cell division process. DNA can also be damaged by exposure to chemicals or radiation, or through oxidative damage. Nature has made provisions with several different systems to correct errors in DNA replication. More than 100 different enzymes are used by the cell to repair the various errors that can arise in the DNA during replication or during the copying process that initiates protein synthesis. Since oxidative stress is one of the main causes of DNA damage, the DNA repair systems of cells can be considered part of the cell's antioxidant defense system (I'll talk more about that in a later chapter.).

Mitochondria

The mitochondria are the energy generators of cells. As such, they are among its most active components. There may be between 1,000 and 2,000 mitochondria in high-energy-producing cells such as muscle, each of them busily producing molecules of adenosine triphosphate (ATP) to power the cell's activities. The reason we need to devote half our diet – half the calories we consume – to carbohydrates or sugars, is that sugars are the preferred fuel for making energy, for building ATP. In every cell, at any given moment, there must be a ready supply of about 1 billion molecules of ATP.

The energy bound in ATP comes from chemical bonds, mainly in carbohydrates. The energy bonds in the ATP are, in turn, used to power cellular activities. As the molecules are recycled, phosphate bonds are made and broken a billion times every two to three minutes. During this process you manufacture and use up several pounds of ATP every 24 hours.

The electron flow that is part of this process generates highly active molecules, called free radicals, in the mitochondria, as oxygen waste products. I'll talk about the negative effects of free radicals on the health of the cell later.

The energy contained in ATP is used in virtually every operation the cell performs. Whenever nutrients are brought into the cell or whenever wastes are excreted; whenever a new molecule is synthesized or degraded, one or more molecules of ATP are used. Whenever you blink, whenever a bird flaps its wings, whenever a firefly flashes in the night, ATP is used. It is truly the universal energy currency of the cell and of almost all life on earth.

The Endoplasmic Reticulum

Everything that happens in the cell relative to proteins – metabolizing amino acids, building proteins, hormones and enzymes – happens in the rough endoplasmic reticulum (RER). The endoplasmic reticulum is a complex membrane network that occupies much of the volume of the cell outside the nucleus. Part of the RER contains small protein complexes, called ribosomes, embedded in the membrane. The ribosomes are analogous to tiny workbenches, where proteins are assembled from amino acid building blocks following the blueprints from the DNA.

The smooth endoplasmic reticulum (SER) is where the fats are metabolized and utilized. Another major role of the SER in the liver is to help maintain a steady level of blood sugar. The liver stores glucose as glycogen in granules associated with the SER and releases it as needed by the body, especially between meals and in response to physical activity. Glycogen is processed in the SER and exported to the bloodstream as needed.

As is the case with many of the cell's organelles, the endoplasmic reticulum performs multiple functions. An especially important additional function of the ER is the conversion of toxic molecules to nontoxic derivatives that can be excreted through the cell membrane. Cells not only demonstrate admirable efficiency (with organelles fulfilling multiple duties) but they also have many backup systems to provide redundancy, similar to auxiliary power generators that allow a business to continue operating seamlessly during a power failure.

Golgi Apparatus

The Golgi apparatus is the shipping department for substances produced in the cell for the body's benefit. Its structure is a series of stacked membranes and associated vesicles and tubules. Whatever is produced in a particular cell – whether it's thyroid hormone or insulin or an antibody – that goes out of the cell through the cell membrane for the use of the other 100 trillion cells in the body, is prepared for transport to other parts of the body in the Golgi apparatus.

Lysosomes

There's an old (very old) joke about the fellow who had an idea for making a million dollars by inventing a cleaning product that could dissolve anything – until he realized he couldn't do that until he invented a bottle he could keep it in. Well, the cell has figured out that trick, in organelles called lysosomes.

Lysosomes come in all sizes, and they contain the enzymes involved with digestion. Lysosomes contain some thirty different enzymes – enzymes that are capable of degrading all major classes of biological materials. In general, lysosomes consist of a dense matrix of phospholipids and proteins, just like any other single membrane in the cell. When the membrane of the lysosome is formed from the ER, however, it is particularly resistant to digestion, a formula which remains a mystery.

We do know that some of the enzymes are not in their fully active form until they come into contact with materials to be digested, another clever trick that the cell performs on a routine basis.

In other parts of the cell, vesicles – tiny balloons formed from single membranes – enclose degenerated organelles. Debris of old mitochondria rendered dysfunctional by oxidative damage is digested by lysosomes. Phagocytic cells engulf bacteria and other foreign agents from outside the cell and package them in vesicles as part of the immune response. The vesicles fuse with the lysosomes containing digestive enzymes, and the material is broken down and then either recycled within the cell or ejected through the cell membrane.

If you've ever been through a strike by sanitation workers, you know what a problem it can be when garbage collection services are halted. Without lysosomes, cells would soon strangle in their own debris.

Lysosomes also play a critical role in the maturation of red blood cells (erythrocytes). These cells begin life as stem cells in the bone marrow, with a full complement of organelles. Once they begin circulation in the bloodstream, erythrocytes lose their nuclei, mitochondria, ribosomes, and many cytoplasmic enzymes as they become highly specialized for carrying oxygen and breaking down glucose. These organelles, no longer needed, are packaged into vesicles and digested by the enzymes in the lysosome.

This process is carried out on a massive scale. In healthy adults, an estimated 10 billion red blood cells are produced each hour. Maturation takes 24 to 48 hours, and their lifetime is about 120 days. Then, they are removed from circulation by phagocytic cells of the spleen and liver.

Peroxisomes

Discovered as separate entities only 30 years ago, a most important organelle is the peroxisome, which contains detoxification enzymes critical in the cell's ability to neutralize all the toxic substances it is exposed to daily. Like mitochondria, peroxisomes consume oxygen, although in smaller amounts. This oxygen is used in various chemical reactions that are associated not with ATP formation but with detoxification.

This activity leads to the production of hydrogen peroxide, a highly reactive free radical. Thus, peroxisomes also contain the antioxidant enzyme catalase, which can neutralize hydrogen peroxide. Without the protective systems in the lysosomes and peroxisomes, the cell would be almost defenseless against the damaging effects of toxins and associated free radicals.

The Cell Membrane

Although often overlooked as a distinct entity, the outer covering of the cell, the cell membrane, is also an organelle and most critical for health. The major constituents of cell membranes are lipids and proteins.

The structure of cell membranes is the lipid bilayer, which is two layers of lipids in which the hydrophobic polar ends face both in toward the center of the cell and outward to the extracellular space. Various proteins are embedded in the membrane, serving as receptors for innumerable substances, such as hormones and neurotransmitters. Further, the membrane contains a variety of channels and ports for pumping specific atoms, such as calcium and sodium, into or out of the cell.

This combination of lipids and proteins in constant movement is often characterized as a "fluid mosaic." To give you an idea of how much we are still learning about the working of the cell membrane, this model had only begun to be developed in the 1970s. Staying abreast of these new developments required me to devote much time to basic research at Gull Laboratories. Being aware of new knowledge of cell membrane immunology and membrane antigenicity was important for me, in order to develop the viral assays that used whole cells.

Another illustration that cell membranes are very dynamic and active structures, in no way static or rigid, is the rate of turnover of membrane constituents. In a living cell, the membrane is in an endless process of renewal and modification. It is a selective process, with the rate of turnover varying for different proteins and lipids. The half-life of some phospholipids in membranes is measured in hours, while protein turnover is usually measured in days.

Membrane turnover is also a process by which the cell continuously removes damaged components. Fatty acids, damaged by oxidation, lose their ability to function as part of the membrane. They must be removed and disposed of by enzymes called lipases to maintain membrane function. Enzymes called proteases carry out a similar process for repair of membrane proteins.

New components of the cell membranes are almost always being synthesized in the endoplasmic reticulum as they are needed. To me, the complexities of determining the needs of specific membranes and assembling the lipid and protein components in proportions to match the momentary needs are as mind-boggling as anything else the cell does. The cell membranes, often regarded as the simplest, least exciting components of the cell, upon closer examination are nothing less than a wonder and a marvel.

Functions of Cell Membranes

Cellular membranes are selectively permeable to small molecules, and this allows the cell to precisely control and main-

The Human Cell

Rough
Endoplasmic
Reticulum

Cell
Membrane

Smooth
Endoplasmic
Reticulum

Nucleus

Lysosome

Mitochondria

Golgi
Apparatus

Peroxisome

tain its internal composition. Only small, uncharged molecules can diffuse freely through the phospholipid bilayers. Small, nonpolar molecules, such as oxygen and carbon dioxide, are soluble in the lipid bilayer and therefore can readily cross from one side of the membrane to the other.

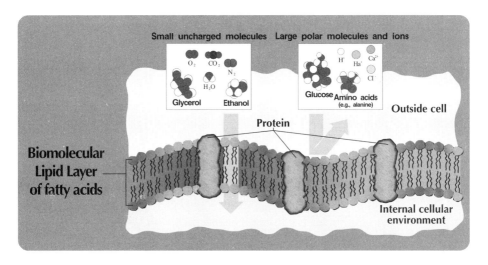

Cellular membranes are selectively permeable.

Small, uncharged polar molecules, such as H_2O, can also diffuse through membranes but large, polar molecules and charged ions cannot. Active modes of transport, which require energy, are necessary to bring such nutrients as glucose into the cell and to expel most waste materials. If nutrients in our food or our supplementation are not in the correct form for absorption, however, they will not be transported across the gut into the bloodstream and therefore will not be available to the cells.

Apoptosis

Although each cell in the body plays an important role for

a time (or else it wouldn't be there) the cells, themselves, know when members of the community of cells are no longer contributing to the well-being of the body and must be eliminated. They accomplish this through a process called apoptosis, a form of "cell suicide."

While in the womb, for example, the fetus manufactures new nerve cells at a tremendous rate, thousands of new ones every minute. Many more are developed than can be used, and the unused neurons must be eliminated, if only to simplify communications between the surviving cells. Some parts of the nervous system lose 85 percent of their neurons to pruning by apoptosis (a process that also creates the separations between our fingers and toes).

In addition to the signals received in the developmental process, the cells themselves seem to recognize when they have been damaged or have otherwise lost function and will generate the initial instructions to begin the apoptotic process themselves. In cancer, this signal becomes switched off by substances and processes we do not fully understand, and precancerous cells that pose a threat to the body begin unlimited growth that leads to a tumor. An important self-protective function of the body is subverted, and the result is deadly disease.

The Next Step

I've said several times that the cell is the fundamental unit of life. But what is life? Ever since the cell theory was first propounded 140 years ago, we have repeatedly returned to the cell in our investigations and speculations on what it means to be a living organism. Many men and women, much wiser than I, have attempted definitions of life, and none of them has proved to be accurate or inclusive.

In this era of the Human Genome Project, we tend to focus too much on the genetic explanation. Genetics isn't the same thing as life. As the sperm cell from the male and the egg from the female meet to form a single cell that divides and eventually develops into an infant, it is clear that much more is involved than genetic coding. There must be other sources of information, of directions for growth and development, for the miracle of a new human to come into being. We can only speculate as to what those sources may be. For the time being, what I've learned from studying cells – cells in cultures and cells in human beings – is that there is more to the cell than science can explain. Human life is too complex to be explained by science and chance.

After he and James Watson had deduced the structure of DNA, Francis Crick announced to a gathering at the local pub that they had "discovered the secret of life." There's no question that they had unveiled a very important mechanism for life. The complementary nature of DNA is necessary to life as we know it on earth, but it isn't enough to fully explain the phenomenon of life itself.

Working with viruses and growing them in cell cultures, I could see that DNA is like a software program; but, I also know that a program by itself has limited value. A virus contains the software for producing its own proteins, yet it lives within the life of a cell. It needs to share in the cell's breath of life for it to have life, itself.

The cell's life element is a miracle – a wondrous event that cannot be fully explained. Although I can see them function with my eyes through my microscope, as an astronomer can see the planets and stars through his telescope, I realize that the cells that compose you and me are, indeed, invisible miracles.

Chapter 6
That Fateful Day

There have been many fateful days in my life, and I expect to encounter many more in the decades ahead. My father's death was a fateful day, as were the days on which my mother and other close family members and friends died. Marvelous fateful days were the days of the births of my son and daughter, whose lives have brought so much meaning and joy to all that I am and do.

My decision to seriously pursue studies and a career in the life sciences instead of music created a different kind of fateful day – the kind of fateful day I classify as a moment of truth, a day of decision, or a fork in the road best traveled. My decision to focus on immunology and infectious diseases was that kind of fateful day, as was the day I launched Gull Laboratories in September of 1974. The success of my viral test kits was largely a result of my ability to grow the healthiest human cells possible in culture, which is why I felt you deserved to experience a taste of Cell Biology 101 a little earlier.

During its first decade, Gull Laboratories enjoyed rapid and steady growth, and I found myself more and more involved in the international scientific community, especially throughout Europe. Largely because of my success in having established the definitive test for the Epstein-Barr virus, I was privileged to be one of the first non-Europeans to be accepted into the European Society for Clinical Virology, the premier association of virology researchers in Europe at the time.

I recall driving from a symposium in the Alsace Lorraine region of France and, as can easily happen on those winding roads that can put you into Germany at any given turn, I lost my way. Or, perhaps, I found my way.

About twenty minutes outside the town of Colmar, I came across a lovely, small village named Gunsbach in the Alsatian Munster valley. There in front of me was the home that Albert Schweitzer constructed in 1928. It is now used to house the museum and archives dedicated to his memory. To this day, I cannot help but feel that he invited me to stop by to share his thoughts.

On the right of the entry is Dr. Schweitzer's study and bedroom, which is kept exactly as he left it the last time he was in Gunsbach, in 1959. In the corner, on a table, is the life-sized reproduction of the head of a native African, the symbol of Schweitzer's lifetime of humble service in his hospital in Gabon, Africa. Over the door of his bedroom is a painting labeled *Veneration Vitae*, which means "reverence for life." This was the principle on which his whole philosophy was based, and a few lines from the famous book he wrote were framed on the wall beside the painting:

The greatest good is to preserve life, to

promote life, to raise life to the highest
value which it is capable of. The greatest
evil is to destroy life, to injure life, to
repress life which is capable of development.

Here was one of the great humanitarians of the twentieth
century, who by the age of 30 had already written three books and
made valuable contributions in the fields of music, religion, and
philosophy. He was an accomplished organist and an authority on
J. S. Bach, a church pastor, the principal of a theological semi-
nary, and a university professor with a doctorate in philosophy.

At the age of 30, aware of the desperate need of Africans
for medical care, and against the advice of nearly all of his colleagues and friends, he took the road less traveled. He decided to
change careers again and become a medical doctor, devoting the
rest of his life to serving thousands of natives in one of the most
remote, undeveloped areas of the world.

In 1913, at the age of 37, Dr. Schweitzer and his wife
opened a hospital in a province of French Equatorial Africa. After
40 years of contributions as "The Jungle Doctor," he was awarded
the Nobel Peace Prize in 1953. He died in 1965, at the age of 90,
still at work in his hospital in Africa.

I'll never forget the special feeling of being in his presence
while sitting quietly in his home and walking around it. On my
way back from France to Gull Laboratories in Salt Lake City, I
marveled at Dr. Schweitzer's being able to understand infectious
diseases, with such a varied and different background. I could
only imagine what more he could have accomplished in his lifetime had he been the beneficiary of modern research on the intri-

cacies and breakthrough discoveries concerning the human cell. He will always be an inspiration as a selfless steward who truly practiced what most of us only preach and who colored brilliantly outside the lines of conventional society.

By the end of the 1980s, I was totally consumed with my work in virology, and it seemed as if there were never enough hours in the days, weeks, or months to learn enough or contribute enough to the mission of my laboratory. As CEO, COO, and director of research at Gull Laboratories, I realized that my energy and endurance were being tested and became keenly aware that my own health was slowly but steadily declining. I had an intuitive feeling that I was a cobbler putting new soles on the shoes of others while having holes in my own shoes.

All I needed to do was look in the mirror to see that I was practicing something quite different from the definition of true health I gave you earlier – being the best one can be with the conditions one is given and the situation in which one lives.

In all the years I've worked with human cells in the laboratory, I've never ceased to be amazed at how wonderful they are in design and function. My fascination with the workings of the cell has never flagged, and I've never taken my work for granted.

When you work with something every day, year after year, it's easy to take yourself out of the picture. Even though I was devoted to helping others regain their health, it was obvious that I had taken my own health for granted. A body is like an automobile in that we don't consider it seriously until it speaks to us by breaking down. My body was definitely speaking to me, and I didn't like what it said.

I was well aware that the infectious diseases that had killed my early ancestors had been replaced in our industrialized society with degenerative diseases. The preponderance of clinical studies concerning cardiovascular disease, cancer, and diabetes and the staggering number of people affected had not gone unnoticed. I knew that heart attacks, stroke, and cancer were killing over a million Americans every year. My silent alarm was sounding.

My father had succumbed to heart disease at age 57. With only a few exceptions, I had watched cancer, heart disease, and diabetes claim aunts and uncles on both sides of the family. My mother was diagnosed with breast cancer in her 60s and endured surgery, radiation, and chemotherapy. It was agonizing for me, as I know it was for her, to watch her fighting valiantly – both the disease and the toxic therapies – to the end. Sadly, even in my own generation, cancer took a further personal toll when it claimed my older brother, Charles. Degenerative disease has definitely plagued my family.

Different people handle problems in different ways; some deny them or hide from them; others surrender to them; some ignore them; many are unaware of them. There are those who make a personal commitment to challenge their problems and overcome them. I decided it was time for another change in the road I was traveling.

The more I learned about oxidative stress and free-radical damage to cells, the more I became convinced that simply improving the quality of my diet and exercising more were not enough. I had sampled and analyzed a so-called balanced diet of good foods, and it wasn't the answer.

One of my closest friends, Terry Frank, who had served on

the board of directors with me at Gull Laboratories, made some suggestions. He was a licensed pharmacist, with his own small chain of pharmacies, and when I asked him for a recommendation on nutritional supplements that would offer the best quality and quantity of ingredients my body needed, he suggested one of the most popular brands on the market. He was a pharmacist, not a nutritionist, so he made no claims about their efficacy other than to say they were supposed to be the best on the market.

I didn't pay much attention to what they were, I was just eager to do anything I could to help myself regain the energy, stamina, endurance, and well-being I had previously enjoyed. One day, while I was sitting at my desk during a phone call, I happened to pick up the plastic bottle containing the supplements and began to read the list of the ingredients and percentages of the contents. I hung up the phone and read the label again, hardly able to believe my eyes.

I ran upstairs to the laboratory and grabbed one of the scientists, exclaiming in dismay: "Look what they're putting into bottles and selling us, calling them nutritional supplements to enhance our health. If we fed this stuff to our cells in this lab, we'd be out of business in no time! They wouldn't survive."

There was no comparison to what the human cell cultures in our laboratories were being fed. When we analyzed the products from a number of different manufacturers and suppliers, many of the products did not even contain what was listed on the labels. The amounts and ratios of different vitamins and minerals were inadequate and out of balance, and some of the ingredients would actually have made the benefits of other ingredients worthless.

On that fateful day I decided to mobilize my resources and jump into the fray. Here was a need that demanded to be met.

Just as viral test kits had filled a critical need for tools to help health-care practitioners diagnose infectious diseases in their patients, so we needed the essential nutrients as tools to help our own cells defend against and repair the damage done to them by infectious and oxidative agents.

Chapter 7
Fighting Degenerative Disease

My new career direction began with my concerns for my own failing health and grew, day by day, into a passion to enhance the health of my family and of all human beings. The global indictment was clear at that time and is even more illuminating today. We simply aren't getting enough nutrients to offset the damage being done to our cells by the environment I've referred to as the toxic cradle.

No matter how or where we shop – in supermarkets or upscale neighborhood groceries – our daily intake of commercially processed foods, grown in nutrient-deficient soils, won't give us the nutrition we need. Plants, like humans, can't create minerals. They absorb them from the earth in which they grow. However, since my boyhood days in North Dakota, most commercial farms have been using nitrogen-phosphate-potassium (NPK) fertilizers on their crops, a practice that has the net result of allowing the other essential nutrients to be depleted from the soil.

To make matters worse, a diet of high-fat, high-sugar fast foods, combined with the declining consumption of fruits and vegetables, is creating a disturbing new population in the industrialized nations called the "Baby Blubber Generation." Obese, yet undernourished! Overweight from the cradle to the grave.

Through my years of experience and study – and poring through stacks of medical journals, scientific research papers, and reports from the World Health Organization – I learned long ago that we had a problem with degenerative diseases that eventually would dwarf the pandemic outbreaks of infectious disease in the past century. The oxidative damage caused by free-radical activity from environmental pollution and poor lifestyle choices has overwhelmed the natural antioxidant defenses within the cells of our bodies. Globally, the situation looks very bleak. Chronic degenerative disease, which kills more than 24 million people a year, is continuing to impose increasing burdens of suffering and disability on hundreds of millions.

For the first time in history, more individuals in industrialized nations are overweight and obese than are of normal weight. Excess weight is directly linked to an increase in cardiovascular disease, stroke, cancer, type 2 diabetes, hypertension, and osteoarthritis.

Atherosclerosis, one type of cardiovascular disease, is caused by, among other factors, the oxidation of LDL cholesterol by excessive free radicals. This life-threatening condition, previously a disease of the elderly, is appearing in children from two to fifteen years of age. In addition, approximately 30 percent of strokes have been associated with elevated homocysteine in individuals having low levels of folic acid and vitamins B6 and B12. Nutrient deficiency and free-radical damage can be considered real global bioterrorists, killing more than 7 million individuals each year through heart disease and nearly 5 million a year by stroke.

Despite great advances in the diagnosis of cancer, the eventual outcome is too often a painful struggle to the end. Medical research has demonstrated a link between cancer and diet, with specific evidence that it develops from accumulated damage to the DNA of the cells by free-radical activity. It doesn't arrive suddenly; it silently stakes its claim through the years. Cancer is taking the lives of over 6 million people annually and, according to the World Cancer Research Fund, 3 to 4 million cases of cancer could be prevented each year through dietary change.

In what could be termed the epidemic of this century, more than 135 million people now suffer from diabetes, and the total worldwide is expected to rise to 300 million by 2025. Diabetics not only have twice the risk for stroke and heart attacks, as well as degeneration in eyesight, kidney, and nerve function, but also account for more than 20,000 non-trauma-related amputations each year. Management of the disease is difficult because it arises mostly from lifestyle issues, including diet, obesity, and lack of exercise.

Diabetes first manifests itself with excess insulin production, followed by the development of insulin resistance in the body. Insulin is the hormone responsible for reducing sugar levels in the blood. The key to prevention is the combination of a low-glycemic diet, fortified with essential fatty acids, nutritional supplementation targeted to enhance insulin sensitivity and optimize antioxidant protection, and regular aerobic exercise. Later, I'll discuss actions you can take in your life, on a daily basis, to prevent or mitigate the serious effects of these diseases.

My concerns about my own health and that of my family, coupled with my understanding of our "toxic cradle" environment and the mounting evidence connecting chronic degenerative disease with oxidative stress and poor nutrition, caused me to make some major, life-changing decisions.

At Gull Laboratories, my scientific team had accepted outside contract work to package nutritional supplements for other companies. Having set the world standard for viral test kits, we were meticulous with respect to product integrity and quality assurance. I had learned many years ago that great science could be destroyed by poor manufacturing, and I've always demanded that our facilities, then and now, meet good manufacturing practices (GMP) for pharmaceutical grade products – standards much higher than those food companies and nutritional supplement companies are required to meet.

In the United States, vitamin manufacturers are required to abide only by the standards set for food. Unfortunately, those standards are not very high. Unclear portioning and labeling are just the beginning of vagueness in food manufacturing. Batches of raw ingredients may not be monitored for contaminants or purity. The manufacturing line may not be controlled to keep out dust, which often contains everything from skin flakes and hair to dust mites and bacteria. In addition, there's a strong possibility that the people running the machines may not be properly trained to control every variable encountered.

When raw ingredients are shipped to my manufacturing facilities, they are immediately quarantined to await a string of elaborate laboratory tests to determine their purity, potency, and quality. Anything that doesn't meet all of our internal criteria is rejected and returned to the supplier. Everything done in quality assurance and manufacturing has a written, detailed procedure. All employees have been trained to follow the book – explicitly. Nothing is left to chance.

But back to my story. When we began testing other health supplements in our laboratory to verify their quality and effectiveness, we were shocked with the inadequacies we found. They were of low quality (synthetic, inorganic, and unnatural), and it was apparent that low-cost manufacturing achieved higher profit margins but resulted in lower-grade products for the consumer. The ingredients also had low bioavailability, which meant that, when you took them, they couldn't get to where they could do you much good. They were formulated in inappropriate nutrient amounts and ratios, and many had incorrect and misleading labels. It was not uncommon for us to see a product labeled as containing 400 milligrams of a particular ingredient, but analysis would show that it actually contained as little as 50 milligrams. In other words, the supplements were totally inadequate in supplying the cells' needs for critical micronutrition that must be supplemented today.

What consumers thought they were buying and what they were receiving were very different. In 1992, I became dedicated to solving the problems of cellular nutrition for the human body with the same passion and persistence I had applied to disease diagnosis at Gull Laboratories. Our ability to grow healthy and vibrant cells was unmatched. I knew what cells needed for growth and repair, and also what would protect them from oxidative damage.

I formed a new company to develop these products and named it USANA, a word with Greek and Latin roots meaning "true health." True health is what I wanted to attain for myself and my family, and this became my most significant challenge in the ensuing decade on the road best traveled.

To focus on the role of nutrition in degenerative diseases, in 1994 I sold my controlling interest in Gull Laboratories to a large German health-care company. At the company's insistence, I agreed to continue to spearhead the development of assays for coronary heart disease, guide research and development, and serve as chairman of the board.

During my decades in the laboratory, all I had had to concern myself with was providing the essential nutrients for growing healthy cells for my viral test kits. But in our everyday lives we are not dealing with cells in a controlled environment. In the world we live in, our cells are exposed to a toxic, uncontrolled environment.

Based on everything I've learned about growing healthy human cells, I recognize that there are only two factors we need to consider to prevent cellular degeneration: nutrient deficiency and oxidative damage. In the next chapter, I'll talk about cellular and human nutrition and then later give you some action ideas for your own lives.

Chapter 8
Cellular Nutrition

The knowledge I gained over the years from studies and, even more, from hands-on experience in virology, immunology, and cell culture resulted in the formulation of a concept that I call "cellular nutrition."

What does that mean? In summary, it means ensuring that the cells of our body receive all the nutrients they need for performing all cellular functions, repairing and regenerating structures, and preventing oxidative damage. The nutrients need to be in the correct forms, the right amounts, and the proper balance. The ideal diet for maintaining healthy cells – and healthy bodies – involves much more than we might expect.

Through many years of research in microbiology and virology, I had seen that nutrition was the major influence on the health of human cells in culture. When I combined that insight with studies on infectious and degenerative diseases, observing how they attacked the body one cell at a time, there was no escaping the conclusion that optimal nutrition at the cellular level had the potential for preventing – and even reversing – degenerative disease.

Constituents of Cells

One way we can gain insight into what is required for optimal cellular nutrition is by looking at what the body and its cells are made of. Starting with the most numerous atoms and working down, the makeup of the average adult human body goes something like this:

Composition of the Human Body

Element	Symbol	(% of atoms in the body)

Major elements: (99.3%)

Hydrogen	H	63%
Oxygen	O	26%
Carbon	C	9%
Nitrogen	N	1%

Major minerals: (0.7%)

Calcium	Ca
Phosphorus	P
Potassium	K (L., *kalium*)
Sulfur	S
Sodium	Na (L., *natrium*)
Chlorine	Cl
Magnesium	Mg

Trace elements: less than 0.01% of total atoms

Boron	B
Iron	Fe (L., *ferrum*)
Iodine	I
Copper	Cu (L., *cuprum*)
Zinc	Zn
Manganese	Mn
Cobalt	Co
Chromium	Cr
Selenium	Se
Molybdenum	Mo
Tin	Sn (L., *stannum*)
Silicon	Si
Vanadium	V

(Adapted from Vander, A. J., Human Physiology, 4th Ed.
New York, NY, McGraw-Hill, 1985)

Most people are surprised to learn how many different elements it takes to make a living body, especially since most of those elements are not ones we tend to associate with life. The truth is that we are of the earth, and the body is composed entirely of the elements from the earth. Hydrogen, carbon, oxygen, and nitrogen predominate, largely because the body is 70 percent water (H_2O), and cell structures of protein and fat are composed of those elements. Importantly, elements found in small or trace amounts are also necessary for life, and they really drive the health and activity of the cell.

Cell Culture Nutrition

The inadequacies of the health supplements we analyzed became apparent when we compared them with what I put into cell culture media. Because the cell is the basic unit of the body, the media had to supply all the nutrients to allow for the cells to manufacture all the structures and perform all the functions. The cell culture media would supply the nutritional needs of the body as well, but for the cells in our bodies, we also have to provide antioxidant protection from the damaging effects of a toxic environment.

In practice, this meant that we start with purified water and add to it all the elements of life – everything the cell needs for life and growth. Comparing the molecular constituents in our media, such as amino acids and fatty acids, with classes of nutrients in the foods we eat, such as proteins and fats, we can see how closely cellular nutrition is related to nutrition for the whole body.

Proteins

It's not easy to choose which is the most important class of macronutrient, but the proteins are certainly the most varied and interesting. Here, except in cases of malnutrition (which I've seen far too much of, especially in children in Eastern Europe), it is not so much a question of quantity as it is of quality. All proteins – some 20,000 different ones in the human body – are made up of amino acids. Nine of the 20 known amino acids are essential, meaning we are unable to manufacture them from other substances ourselves and must get them from our food.

The action of many proteins, especially enzymes, depends upon their three-dimensional structure. Even before it is fully synthesized on the ribosomes, the long string of amino acids that makes up an average protein begins to twist and curl upon itself, eventually achieving a shape that permits it to operate on a substrate in a very specific manner.

Even the smallest error can cause major problems. The hemoglobin protein and sickle-cell anemia provide a good example. The hemoglobin molecule picks up oxygen from our lungs, carries it in our bloodstream, and releases it where it is needed. A complete hemoglobin molecule acts rather like four pairs of pincers in one assembly. It snaps closed around four oxygen molecules, holding the molecules in its jaws as it travels through the bloodstream to the capillaries. There, it releases the oxygen molecules in an area of low oxygen concentration.

Sickle-cell anemia is the result of a single base-pair error in the genetic code for hemoglobin. The difference between a person with sickle-cell anemia and a healthy person is the second "letter" of the sixth "word" in the beta gene. The gene says "CAC," specifying valine, when the normal sequence is "CTC," which codes for glutamic acid. One base-pair error, and the misconstructed protein molecules interact with each other to form fiber-like structures that distort the red blood cell membrane into sickle shapes and other bizarre forms. These formations result in the blockage of the capillaries, with associated tissue damage, and the destruction of the deformed red blood cells, with consequent anemia.

Although sickle-cell anemia is a genetic disorder, it is a good example of how only a small error is needed to cause serious malfunctioning in the body. There are many different reactions in the human body in which a shortage of a certain nutrient – an amino acid, for example – can cause problems that are just as serious. In most cases, when there is a deficiency of an amino acid, the protein simply isn't manufactured by the cell. Then, structures requiring that protein are either impaired or important cellular functions fail to occur.

I hope I haven't lost you. I sometimes do that in my lectures. I get so engrossed in, and enthusiastic about, our research and its significance to everyday life that it is a challenge to describe what we are doing in everyday language.

When we say *protein* many people think immediately of meat or dairy. But plants should be our number one source of protein. The amount of dietary protein we need daily is much smaller than most people think: only about 50 grams for men and 40 for women, which is about half what we thought 20 years ago. That's a portion about the size of a deck of cards.

We can easily get that amount from plant foods as well as animal foods. Perhaps the best choice is a combination of the two, with meat used almost as a condiment, for flavoring, rather than for its protein content. That way you can get the protein your cells need without the cholesterol, saturated fats, hormones, antibiotics, and accumulated toxic chemicals virtually all living creatures are laced with these days.

Vitamins

As their name suggests, vitamins are absolutely vital to life. They perform hundreds of critical roles in the body. As important as they are, however, the body is unable to manufacture them, and we must obtain them from our diet. Let's take a look at just one representative of this category of nutrient, to see how critical it is to be sure that your diet includes an adequate supply. We'll review vitamin B1

Vitamin B1, or thiamin, is found in every tissue in the body; the heart, liver and kidneys have the highest concentrations. Severe thiamin deficiency can lead to beriberi, a metabolic disorder that interferes with the function of the brain, nerves, and muscles. Milder deficiencies are manifested primarily as disorders of the neuromuscular, gastrointestinal and cardiovascular systems. The symptoms of a deficiency in vitamin B1 include depression, memory loss, indigestion, weight loss, anorexia, edema, muscular weakness, rapid pulse, and defective muscular coordination.

Vitamin B1 plays several critical roles in the cell and in the body. Most important for cellular metabolism, it functions as coenzyme TPP to help convert glucose into energy – thus it is required by every cell in the body. Altogether, vitamin B1 acts as a coenzyme essential to at least four different processes by which your body extracts energy from carbohydrates.

Thiamin is also necessary for proper nerve transmission and for the maintenance of muscular function, especially in the heart. It is also required for the synthesis of acetylcholine, a primary neurotransmitter, and is involved in the synthesis of fatty acids.

All this is driven by the presence or absence of one substance, which is incapable of being produced by the body and must be supplied by the diet. It's hard to imagine that this one substance is responsible for so many aspects of health, that a deficiency of it can result in so much cellular degeneration. Yet, a lack of vitamin B1 is one of the most common nutritional deficiencies in humans. A U.S. Department of Agriculture study reported that 45 percent of Americans consume less than the Recommended Daily Allowance (RDA) of thiamin.

There are several reasons why so many of us are deficient in vitamin B1, which is found in whole-grain products, green vegetables, potatoes, and nuts. Unfortunately, it is easily destroyed or lost during cooking, being both heat-sensitive and water-soluble. It is depleted by diuretic drugs and antibiotics as well as by such gastrointestinal disturbances as diarrhea. Moreover, many people absorb thiamin poorly because of lactose intolerance and celiac disease (gliadin, or wheat sensitivity).

Virtually every vitamin we added to the culture medium performs a multitude of critical cellular functions. We can't afford to short-change ourselves of any of them.

Minerals

All minerals come from the earth; none can be made in the cells. Again, let's take a look at only one of the essential minerals to see why we include it in the cell culture medium and why it's important to our health.

Calcium is the most abundant mineral in the body and certainly one of the most important. At the cellular level, calcium affects cell wall permeability, regulating the passage of fluids across the membrane, and functions in cell adhesion.

The body employs no fewer than three different regulatory systems to control levels of blood calcium. If levels drop too low, absorption in the intestines increases, the bones release stored calcium, and the kidneys reduce the rate of calcium excretion.

Calcium is the major structural component of bones, and an inadequate intake of calcium is a major factor in the epidemic of osteoporosis that is sweeping the developed nations of the world. The unhealthy Western diet – high in saturated fats, salts, animal proteins, and sugars that form acidic waste products – leaches our most alkaline minerals from our bones, and is the primary cause of osteoporosis. Women, beginning in the teen years, need sufficient calcium intake to promote optimal bone density and prevent excessive bone thinning in later years. Adequate levels of vitamin D and regular weight-bearing exercise also play a role in preventing osteoporosis. Complicating the situation is the fact that the correct balance of magnesium is critical for the metabolism of calcium and vitamin D.

Low levels of calcium in the blood are also associated with high blood pressure – and not just for the person taking the calcium. Clinical data show that when a pregnant woman maintains her blood calcium at healthy levels, her baby's blood pressure stays lower than average for at least the first seven years of life. This usually results in a lower risk of high blood pressure later in life.

Trace Elements

Manganese is an example of one of the trace elements needed by our cells. Manganese is a cofactor that aids in the activation of a wide variety of enzyme systems and is involved in energy production, protein metabolism, and bone formation, as well as the synthesis of L-dopamine and cholesterol. In manganese deficiency, we see impaired growth, especially decreased bone growth, impaired reproductive function, impaired glucose tolerance, and alterations in carbohydrate and lipid metabolism.

The total body content of manganese is only 15 to 20 mg, but we need about 4 mg in the diet every day. Absorbed man-

ganese is rapidly excreted into the gut through bile production and
then lost in the feces. Thus, the need for a daily supply of manganese is not due, so much, to high use as it is to the rapid
turnover of this mineral in the body.

Fats

Fats, or lipids, are the most important components of our
cell membranes. Along with proteins, they form the predominant
structures of our cells and, consequently, our bodies. The brain is
the most lipid-rich tissue we have – 60 percent. The essential fatty
acids (EFAs) are those the body cannot make: linoleic acid (LA),
an omega-6 fatty acid, and linolenic acid (LNA), an omega-3 fatty
acid.

In addition to their structural role in cell membranes, these
EFAs are a major component of bile and are important in cell signal-
ing, both in steroid hormones (for example, estrogen and testos-
terone) and in messenger molecules that convey signals from cell
surface receptors to targets inside the cell.

The ratio of omega-3 to omega-6 fatty acids in the diet is
also important; however, modern food processing methods yield
foods which contain too many omega-6 fatty acids in proportion
to omega-3 fatty acids.

Carbohydrates

We add glucose to the cell culture medium because it is the
preferred fuel for cells to power all their activities. The liver can
convert other carbohydrates, as well as protein, into glucose and
can convert fats into ketone bodies for fueling the mitochondria.
Unfortunately, the metabolism of ketone bodies leaves toxic
residues.

Proteins are not only the least efficient, but the dirtiest cellular fuel, generating the most toxic waste products. Clean-burning carbohydrates are, by far, the best fuel for producing ATP to power the cell. Plant-based carbohydrates are required by the body in larger amounts than any other nutrient.

Hormones and Growth Factors

All cells need hormones and growth factors, but many of the hormones and growth factors are made only by specialized cells. For example, although it is synthesized only in the pancreas, insulin is required by every cell in the body. Growth factors are highly specific proteins that stimulate cell division in particular types of cells.

Water

The human body is made up of cells – and water. In fact, almost 70 percent of the weight of the body is due to water.

Water is a truly amazing chemical. It can dissolve most substances, so it is close to being a universal solvent. That makes it an excellent medium for transporting nutrients and oxygen to the cells. Chemical reactions tend to occur readily in water, so it's an excellent environment for the body's essential chemical interactions. Water has unusual thermic properties, which help the body maintain a stable temperature. Put simply, water is an essential component in virtually every function the body performs.

To grow healthy cells in culture, the water in the culture medium must be purified. Cell-culture water can be prepared by distillation, ion exchange and carbon filtration, or reverse osmosis. Because of the amount of pollution in our water supplies today, along with chlorine and in some cases fluoride, you should drink only purified water. Treatment plants for public water supplies add scores of chemicals to disinfect the water. Our deepest ground waters, today, are polluted with agricultural and industrial wastes that have been dumped onto the ground and have seeped into the water supply. Avoid tap water and find a supply of purified water, for the sake of your cells. Mineral waters can be substituted but should be used only if purified water is not available.

Environmental Threats

A little over a decade ago, I came realize that cells degenerate for two reasons: nutrient deficiency and oxidative damage. With a few modifications, following the guidelines for nutrition at the cellular level takes care of the nutrient deficiencies. That leaves us with the second, but perhaps most important, factor in the health of the cells – oxidative damage.

The cells that we culture in the laboratory with such good nutrition are in a carefully regulated environment. It is an artificial environment compared to the environment the cells in our bodies are subjected to every day. They aren't exposed to the toxins that are in the air, the water, and the food that we choose to eat. They are not subject to the stress that we have made a major part of our working lives and even part of our family life and leisure time.

Oxidative damage – it's all due to electrons, those tiniest components of atoms that amount to not much more than infinitesimal scraps of energy. Electrons (and the charges they carry) bond atoms together to form molecules and are involved in chemical reactions.

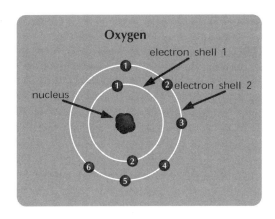

The structure of the oxygen atom includes a nucleus and two electron shells.

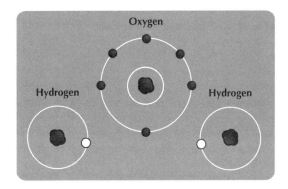

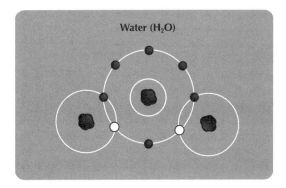

Electrons in the outer shells of oxygen (O) and hydrogen (H) are shared to form a stable molecule.

Electrons "orbit" atoms in one or more shells, forming a cloud around the atom. The innermost shell is full when it contains two electrons. When the first shell is full, the electrons begin to fill the second shell, until it contains a full complement of eight electrons. Then the third shell begins to be filled, and so on.

The number of electrons in its outermost shell is the most important feature of an atom for determining its chemical behavior. Because of the electrical and magnetic forces generated by electrons, an element that has a relatively empty outer shell tends to be highly reactive, while an element that has a full outer shell tends not to enter into chemical reactions (is inert). Atoms always prefer a state of maximum stability; an atom with spaces available for electrons will gain or lose electrons to fill or empty its outer shell. It will also share electrons by bonding with other atoms to complete this shell. By sharing electrons, the atoms are bound together and satisfy the conditions of maximum stability for the molecule. For example, oxygen and hydrogen are both very active and unstable elements. When they join together, a very stable compound is formed – H_2O, or water.

How Free Radicals are Formed

Normally, chemical bonds don't split leaving a molecule with an odd, unpaired electron. When bonds are weak, however, splitting can happen, forming free radicals (molecules with unpaired electrons). Free radicals are very unstable – more of a momentary process than a state – and they react quickly with other compounds, trying to capture the needed electron to regain stability.

Generally, free radicals attack the nearest stable molecule, especially if it has a readily available electron in an outer shell that can be stolen. The molecule that is attacked for its electron can become a free radical itself. This can begin a chain reaction; once the process is started, it can cascade and spread in all directions. The result can be a major disruption of a living cell.

Oxidative Damage to Cells

Each cell of the body is bombarded with an estimated 10,000 hits by free radicals every day. Every structure in the cell, every protein and lipid, is susceptible to damage and, consequently, degeneration. Also, every substance produced by the cell – whether enzyme, protein, hormone, or lipid – is also susceptible. Nothing is immune to free-radical oxidative damage.

For example, the phospholipids that compose the fluid mosaic of the cell membranes have long tails of fatty acids. Free

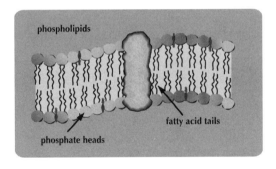

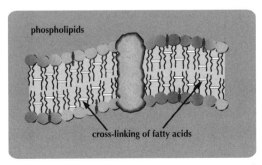

Cross-linking between fatty acids can be caused by free radicals.

radicals can cause cross-linking between fatty acids. This cross-linking can cause the membranes to become rigid, reducing their ability to perform normal functions and decreasing their rate of renewal. Such cross-linking is involved in the plaque formation that is a major factor in the development of atherosclerosis.

The double helix that is the normal configuration of DNA allows for exact copying in replication and accurate transcription during protein synthesis. Free-radical activity can cause the formation of DNA adducts which deform the DNA, causing errors in copying or halting transcription altogether. In fact, DNA deterioration due to oxidative damage may be the most important contributor to the cancer process.

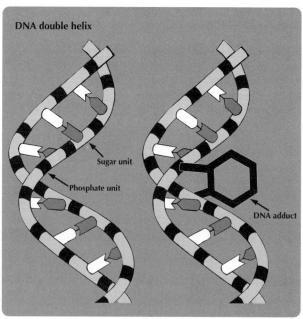

Oxidative damage causes the creation of DNA adducts in the cell's genetic material.

The Need for Antioxidants

As I mentioned earlier, free radicals are generated during normal cell function and metabolism. All cells, especially liver cells, produce free radicals in the process of detoxification. The cells of the body's immune system create free radicals to attack viruses and bacteria. Muscle cells generate great amounts, especially during strenuous exercise. The production of energy in the mitochondria requires the movement of electrons from one molecule to another. Most often this is done in an orderly manner, but at times electrons are lost and free radicals are formed. A free radical is a waste product of the oxidation process that is the predominant chemical activity in every cell.

Environmental factors such as pollution, radiation, cigarette smoke, or heavy metals can also spawn free radicals. These exogenous sources of oxidative stress are steadily increasing and are the reason for the emergence of degenerative disease in the past century.

Normally, human cells can handle the free radicals generated by physiological activity. If the production of free radicals becomes excessive, or a sufficient supply of natural antioxidants is not available, oxidative damage can occur. Of particular importance to long-term health is the oxidative damage that accumulates with age. Today's toxic environment is overwhelming our wonderful innate antioxidant systems, requiring us to supplement with antioxidants. That is the key difference between the cells in your body and the cultured cells that are protected in the laboratory from environmental influences.

In all my twenty years of experience with culturing cells, I never observed a condition where their natural antioxidant defense systems were unable to cope with the generation of free radicals. No matter how fast, or how long some of the cell lines continued to replicate, the cells were able to control for oxidative damage.

Unfortunately, unhealthy lifestyles and toxic environmental conditions now present our cells with far more oxidative stress than they can cope with, especially when denied adequate nutrition. Only with optimal levels of antioxidants can our cells and bodies defend themselves in today's toxic world – supplementation is essential.

How Antioxidants Protect against Free-Radical Damage

Antioxidants, particularly the antioxidant enzymes, such as the superoxide dismutases (SOD), can neutralize free radicals by donating one of their own electrons. This action has the effect of halting the electron-stealing chain reaction. The antioxidant nutrients themselves don't become free radicals when they donate an electron because they are relatively stable in either form. This neutralization of free-radical activity is called scavenging, and active antioxidants are called free-radical scavengers. They prevent further oxidation that could lead to cellular damage and disease. Exogenous antioxidants from the diet can also reduce the level of generation of new free radicals and raise the capacity of the cell's innate oxidation defense systems.

Vitamin E refers to a group of compounds, the tocopherols and tocotrienols, that are the most abundant fat-soluble antioxidants in the body. They are the most widely distributed antioxidants in nature, found in both the plant and animal kingdoms.

Vitamin C is the most abundant water-soluble antioxidant

in the body. Vitamin C also regenerates oxidized vitamin E to its active form. This capability is of particular value in combating free-radical formation caused by pollution and cigarette smoke.

Other important antioxidant defense mechanisms in the body include beta-carotene – the precursor of vitamin A – and uric acid. Some minerals, such as zinc, copper, manganese and selenium, also demonstrate antioxidant activity, particularly as part of the SOD and glutathione enzyme systems.

The generation of free radicals is part of the living process, and the moderation and control of their activity is also essential for life. In the controlled environment of cell cultures, supplementation with antioxidants is not required, but for organisms living in the fouled nest that humans have caused on this earth, supplementation with antioxidants is now critically important.

The vitamins we added to our cell culture media are among the most important antioxidants, but we supplied them in small amounts for nutritional purposes only. Antioxidant doses were not needed.

Cell Regeneration

When things get bad enough, we sometimes have to give up and start over. The same goes for the cells in our body. In Chapter 5, we briefly reviewed the remarkable ability of the cells to regenerate themselves, whether on a steady basis to cope with the rigors of daily life or to recover from disease or trauma.

Each type of cell has specific needs to fulfill in the body and specific nutritional requirements that will allow it to do this. Red blood cells – with an average lifespan of only four months –

must be replaced by the billions every day. Adequate amounts of iron, folic acid, and vitamin B12, plus the necessary proteins and other constituents, must all be present for the body to replace each one of these cells.

The billions of new skin cells that we generate steadily, day and night, last only about a week on average. Vitamin A is one of the most important nutrients for healthy skin and must be supplied in adequate amounts every day. Calcium is the single most important component of healthy bones; but, magnesium, boron, vitamin D, and silicon are also essential to the maintenance of a healthy skeletal system.

When the body must repair itself after disease, trauma, or insult from the environment, there are additional requirements for nutrients. Internal organs, such as the pancreas, must occasionally regenerate cells, especially after inflammation. The lungs, constantly exposed to pollutants in the air drawn in during breathing, steadily shed old and damaged epithelial cells. Wound healing requires the interaction of several kinds of cells, including the rapid migration of newly developed epithelial cells into the traumatized area and the self-sacrifice of macrophages, cells that engulf foreign substances in the wound area, engorging themselves to the point of death.

Nutrition in the Real World

To sum up, the cells of our bodies need optimal nutrition to perform their varied and complex functions. The different types of cells in the body are specialized to perform particular tasks and, thus, may have different nutritional requirements. In addition, compared to cells growing in laboratory cultures, the cells in our bodies need larger amounts of some nutrients to help them deal with environmental stresses. This is the level of nutrition that has been developed at USANA Health Sciences.

Chapter 9
Still Another Fork in the Road

With Gull Laboratories effectively behind me, I found myself with a nagging sense of restlessness, despite the success of USANA and the time and effort the newer company required. USANA was a source of great satisfaction to me. Nowhere else in the world, as far as I knew, were nutritional products of such quality being produced. I had every reason to be satisfied with that, but I knew the war against degenerative disease was not yet won, and I needed to be certain it was being fought on all fronts.

Then – by another one of those strokes of fate that make you wonder just how closely you are being watched from above – I happened to learn about the Strauss estate, just south of Rosarito Beach in Baja California, Mexico. Conrad and Beryl Strauss, of the Levi Strauss family, had purchased property overlooking the Bahia del Descanso (Bay of Rest) and had built a mansion there. Conrad had critical health issues, and they extensively researched the various factors that would contribute to the best health environment in which he could live out his remaining years. With the resources to live just about anywhere in the world, they had chosen this spot. After Conrad's passing, Beryl returned to the eastern U.S. to be with her family and friends.

I decided to purchase the property for conversion into a new kind of medical facility. Sanoviv would be an example of what a health and healing center could be if the newest advances in nutrition and detoxification were employed and if a holistic approach to the body and the patient was made the basis of diagnosis and treatment. Without being fully aware of what I was getting myself into, I had begun to formulate the next phase of my journey along the road best traveled.

During the negotiations with lawyers and real estate agents, I heard about studies that NASA and the Scripps Institute had done on the site. They indicated that it has an unusual combination of climatic, geophysical, atmospheric, and geomagnetic factors that did, indeed, make it a unique location for health and healing. The Strausses had made a very good choice.

But the scientific data were not what convinced me that this was the place. One moody, overcast day I visited the residence on my own, without real estate people. On previous visits I had been very aware of a powerful sense of peace and calm that overcame me as soon as I walked onto the property, and I wanted to investigate further. That day, when I was not distracted by others, the feeling was stronger than ever.

I walked down the slope to the edge of the cliff, beckoned by a caressing breeze off the ocean. Looking down, I saw the tide pools appear as the ocean slowly withdrew, exposing in each pool one of nature's most wonderful ecosystems.

I looked up to see a brown pelican floating regally along the coastline, riding the breeze so efficiently that it rarely needed to flap its wings. Before I knew it, this great, calm, majestic bird was right there in front of me. In that startled moment, as we made eye contact, it spoke to me: "We have been waiting for you. . . . Yes . . . *Yes* . . . This is it . . . *This is it* . . . *We have been waiting for you.*"

How much all of this was due to my imagination is debatable (and unimportant), but the message was clear and unmistakable. This place was special, and I would be part of its destiny. Even the surfers, who hung out on the point just west of the site, spoke of the "good vibes" that drew them to this place over many other prime surfing areas.

Then the clouds broke and let through the sun – close to setting – on my right. That's when I first realized that the site faced not west, as you might expect looking over the Pacific in Baja, California, but directly south, into the Bay of Rest. That meant the sun would describe an arc over the property, bathing it in life-powering energy and regenerating warmth all day long, all year long.

The Strauss discovery was to have a new destiny.

Within weeks, the purchase was complete, and I began to consult friends and colleagues on the design of Sanoviv Medical Retreat, explaining as best I could my vision of what it should be. Both Gull Laboratories and USANA had been ahead of the curve when I founded them, but Sanoviv was a step still further – too far, perhaps, for many people to understand what I felt needed to be done. Gull had developed diagnostic tests with triple the lifespan of most medical products, USANA introduced a level of nutritional supplementation that was unavailable anywhere and Sanoviv would create a concept of medicine, healing, and wellness that many people talked about, but few seriously thought possible.

USANA Health Sciences was founded on the concept of optimal nutrition for long-term good health. It provided the answers for resolving nutritional deficiencies and protection from oxidative damage. Sanoviv would take the nutritional principles of USANA into the clinical arena of the seriously compromised. It would, by using methods of detection and diagnosis too futuristic for acceptance by the medical establishment, open a new realm of therapeutic opportunities. Through new and accurate identification of toxic substances and system disturbances, we would be able to develop detoxification protocols to remove these barriers to healing. Through my design, Sanoviv would provide the most toxic-free environment technologically possible to free – to encourage – the natural healing abilities and processes of the body.

Over the last ten years I have received firsthand accounts of the magic that optimal supplementation can work on an individual's state of health. Every time I meet with large groups is an occasion for more people to express thanks for the difference in their lives that our nutrition has made. The health improvements I have seen have put joy in my soul.

Over time, however, I began to realize that there are situations in which nutritional supplements, however powerful, may not be all that is needed to reverse certain diseases that have already taken hold in the body. Cancer, perhaps, presented the most serious challenge to achieve reversal. I also saw that it is imperative to address all aspects of the individual, if true healing is to occur. It is impossible to heal the body of serious disease without including the mental, emotional, and spiritual aspects of health.

The challenges of the emerging neurodegenerative diseases would require new technological discoveries to drive delivery of antioxidants, natural chelators, displacement elements, and repair nutrients across the blood-brain barrier. Toxic substances that violated the blood-brain barrier would, perhaps, require still more aggressive strategies.

The first consideration in the design and construction of Sanoviv was to provide an environment for guests that was free of negative environmental influences. I knew there would be those whose healing would be predicated on a nontoxic environment. Similar to the cell culture environment of human cells growing in flasks inside temperature-controlled incubators, for healing to occur we may need an environment free of toxins, a place where there are no disturbance foci. One of the main reasons Sanoviv was created was to create a safe haven, an incubator for human bodies analogous to a cell culture incubator environment.

Throughout the conception, design, and construction of Sanoviv, every conceivable care was taken to ensure the entire facility was free of all known environmental toxins and pollutants. All of the building materials, including the paint, stains, glues, and even the stone and tile groutings, were controlled for toxicity. The grounds were covered with virgin topsoil that was assayed for toxins before being brought in from outside.

More than a thousand pieces of furniture and wood structures were built to my specifications with woods I selected. All the upholstery materials are made of untreated, natural fibers. All rugs and pads are custom manufactured. The lighting fixtures in all guest areas are low-voltage, and the electrical wiring through-out is specially designed insulation to eliminate electromagnetic radiation. I know of no other facility in which the body is so free from damaging environmental forces.

Protected from additional accumulation of toxic influences, the body then must be rid of the existing toxins acquired over years of unhealthy living. Living in this toxic world, we have messed up our bodies so badly – biochemically, electrically, meta-bolically, mentally and hormonally – that we must download the lifetime accumulation of toxins before cell repair, rejuvenation, and healing can occur.

Through our lifestyles and the preservatives and toxic chemicals in the foods we eat, we've poisoned the gut such that we cannot absorb essential nutrients properly. There are those who cannot get well, even with the finest nutritional system, because of the burden of environmental toxins in the cells of their body. I believe a program of detoxification needs to become a part of every person's life. But careful guidance is needed to safely mobilize and download life's accumulated toxins, especially those of the head, without relocating them to other parts of the body. This detoxification program is incorporated into all the medical programs at Sanoviv.

The next component of the Sanoviv approach was a focus on painstakingly thorough diagnostics – the most extensive diag-nostic regimen to be found anywhere. Throughout my career in biomedicine, I have insisted that you can't effectively treat the patient unless you know the exact cause or causes of the illness.

So, at this point I needed a complete laboratory, as well as guest rooms, and assessment and therapy rooms. The project was growing – rapidly. Originally, what I had in mind was a relatively modest remodeling of the existing mansion, perhaps adding a floor to one of the wings as a residence for guests. I recall Dr. Denis Waitley saying, when he first saw the Strauss mansion, "It's a fix-up, touch-up, and wax-the-floors kind of project."

My son, David, soon described it as "a project totally out of control." A complete remodeling of the existing mansion had materialized, along with a nine-story residence tower and a medical center, surgical suite, dental theaters, emergency and imaging departments, intensive care and specialized therapy areas, as well as a full complement of massage suites and a complete spa. My only response to David was, "It had to be . . . what it had to be."

As you might expect, I was very gratified when Sanoviv Medical Retreat received full medical and hospital accreditation from the Mexican government shortly after we began operations.

As the project expanded, I insisted on maintaining control of every detail that would affect the well-being of future guests. The alignment of all the structures was determined only after extensive consultations with Feng Shui experts. Even the heads of the beds face magnetic north.

Sanoviv is now a community unto itself, with its own water purification system, sewage treatment facilities, and power-generation capabilities. The reverse-osmosis water purification system provides cell-culture grade water to every faucet in the complex, including all showers and tubs. The emergency power generators can supply the entire project with electrical power in case of outages.

The full scope of Sanoviv Medical Retreat took shape

when I finalized my plans for diagnostic and treatment options. At Sanoviv we have developed an innovative 6-point treatment program that includes cutting-edge medical and dental care, therapeutic nutrition, physical detoxification and cleansing, psychological and spiritual support, fitness, and healing massage and bodywork. Every guest is provided with a personalized comprehensive program that addresses the mind, body, and spirit.

Physical fitness is a very important part of the mix. Any healing process is going to be enhanced by improved fitness of the whole body. For Sanoviv, I wanted a fitness program that emphasized moderate, enjoyable movement in a stimulating, yet peaceful, environment, modeled after stylish European centers. Fitness is not just about working out; at Sanoviv guests learn about the role of the lymphatic system in cleansing the body and releasing toxins even during stretching, resistance training, and cardiovascular fitness training. I believed that each guest should have a personalized fitness program, both during the stay at Sanoviv and after returning home.

Following the dictum of "a sound mind in a healthy body" that the ancients considered key to health, I determined that Sanoviv would have an entire department dedicated to psychospiritual aspects of health and to resolving toxic emotions and memories. The Sanoviv psychospiritual program creates a gentle, nonthreatening environment in which guests can address the mental, emotional, and spiritual components of health and learn to create balance on all levels. Guests learn techniques for stress management, develop healthy coping strategies, and increase self-awareness and self-esteem. Here, too, each guest learns to integrate health-promoting thoughts, emotions, and behaviors into daily life during the stay at Sanoviv and upon return to home life.

Nutrition, of course, is the foundation of the healing therapies at Sanoviv. Both whole foods and advanced nutritional supplementation are employed for detoxification and healing. The plant foods are organically or hydroponically grown on our farm in a pristine mountain valley an hour from Ensenada. Nutrition classes emphasize the importance of modifying food intake to support the body's natural quest for good health. Guests learn how to create a new, healthier relationship with food that will last a lifetime.

Although diet and lifestyle are accepted as major causes of degenerative disease even in established medicine, there is absolute disagreement and confusion on what is correct: low fat? low carbohydrate? low protein? high protein? The average consumer is completely baffled over what is valid and what is not.

Sanoviv is meant to sort out the confusion and clearly reveal to the world what needs to occur for the body to heal itself. We have learned that most medical interventions, such as pharmaceuticals and surgery, do not cure, but rather complicate, the healing process. In contrast to the chemical and mechanical approach that has been the focus of medicine in the past, I believe there are powerful influences on the body from other factors – including the spirit – that we don't fully understand. Sanoviv is exploring these factors to learn how to use them to promote health and healing.

The best part is that we are making a difference. Sanoviv is saving lives and is adding years of productive living to the lives of its guests. In a recent review of all admissions with symptomatic degenerative disease, I saw that Sanoviv may have the finest record of successful disease outcomes, reversals, and improvements of quality of life of any medical facility in existence. Furthermore, I expect that, in time, our successful long-term outcomes will surpass all currently used modalities in allopathic medicine for degenerative disease.

Sanoviv is adding evidence to my conviction that healthy lifestyles, including optimal nutrition, are key to long-term good health, and apply to the reversal of all degenerative diseases – even those which, in conventional medicine, are considered incurable. I have poured my heart and soul into this endeavor. For me, Sanoviv will extend the world of difference that is being made by USANA. Sanoviv was designed for all who want to improve their health, no matter where they are in the spectrum of cellular degeneration. Sanoviv is a place where miracles – invisible and visible – are allowed to happen.

Chapter 10
Take Charge of Your Health

Knowledge, by itself, isn't worth much. Only when you take action and put knowledge to work to benefit others does it have any value. All that I've learned in a lifetime of study would mean nothing except for the good that it has produced through Gull Laboratories, USANA Health Sciences, and Sanoviv Medical Retreat. The most valuable knowledge of all is that which allows you to actively apply what you have learned to improve and maintain your health.

I can give you recommendations that are fully compatible with what I know about the cell and that draw upon that knowledge to the fullest extent possible. I pass these recommendations on to you with one goal in mind, and that is to give you the power to take charge of your health.

I can't say it often enough. The cell is the fundamental unit of life, and proper cellular function is the essence of health. I concluded long ago that, in designing a healthy lifestyle, our goal ought to be to identify nutritional patterns, physical activity regimens, and other factors that directly promote cellular health. In other words, we need to live our lives in ways that support robust cell growth, that promote proper cell functioning, that minimize cellular damage from free radicals and other stressors, that allow cells to repair themselves when damage occurs, and that support cell death (apoptosis) as needed.

Taking Charge of Your Health

It is almost a contradiction in terms, but today's health-care system is overwhelmingly disease-focused. About 98 percent of our total health-care expenditures go to treating and "curing" people who are sick, while only about 2 percent go toward the primary prevention of disease – keeping people healthy. We spend hundreds of billions of dollars annually to prescribe pain medications, replace hips, and bypass arteries. We spend far too little in prescribing lifestyle changes that might prevent disease in the first place. In short, our health-care system is reactive rather than proactive. This situation is unacceptable.

Clearly, there is a place for curative medicine in our health-care system. Acute infections, acute injuries, and acute diseases of many types call for acute approaches to treatment. At the same time, our cure-focused approach to health care has let us down, particularly in the arena of degenerative disease. To date, there are few, if any, routine and effective cures or even long-term treatments for heart disease, cancer, type 2 diabetes, osteoporosis, macular degeneration, or such neurodegenerative diseases as multiple sclerosis, Parkinson's or Alzheimer's disease. With the current health-care system, once you develop a chronic condition, you will likely suffer from it and be limited by it—for life.

The good news is that most – if not all – of these degenerative diseases are preventable. Estimates indicate that some 75 percent, if not more, of all current cases of heart disease, cancer, osteoporosis, type 2 diabetes, cataracts, and macular degeneration could have been prevented through proper nutrition, proper exercise, avoidance of smoking, and so forth. We can greatly improve our prospects for long-term good health by choosing to adopt that type of lifestyle.

No doubt, healthy lifestyles would be much easier for all of us to practice if the medical establishment, especially the large pharmaceutical companies, had their priorities reversed to place prevention ahead of cure. The reduction in pain and suffering would be tremendous. It sounds simple, but that reversal would be nothing less than a revolution in medicine.

Unfortunately, that is still a dream. I wish I could be optimistic about the short-term future of our health-care system, but I'm not. Change of the type that I am proposing will eventually take place, but the monumental inertia that exists in today's health-care bureaucracy will prevent anything from happening soon. I'm afraid it will be years, if not decades, before the proactive approaches of preventive health care play a dominant role in our system of health care.

What do we do in the meantime? We need to take charge of our own health and determine our own fate. We need to embrace, on a personal level, the principles of preventive health care. We need to adopt the lifestyle elements that are now known to dramatically reduce the risk of chronic degenerative disease. We need to start today; and, just as important, we need to encourage our children, our siblings, our parents, and our friends to do the same.

Take charge of your health. This is easier said than done for most of us. But it can be done, and it is imperative that we do it. I see the process happening in three stages.

Stage I
Committing to Health

This first phase lays the foundation for everything else to come. It involves making a personal commitment to being healthy. Ask yourself: *How valuable is my health to me? How do I keep it?* You can choose to be healthy; you can choose to live your life in ways that promote long-term health and dramatically reduce the risk of chronic degenerative disease. Here are the steps:

- Get passionate about your health. Don't take it for granted. Treat it as the precious gift that it is. It's our most valuable asset, a gift from God. Keep in mind that if you don't have your health, virtually everything else in life is diminished. Understand that, on average, by age 65, you have a 50 percent chance of suffering from a significant disability due to chronic disease; but you don't have to be one of those statistics. By adopting a healthy lifestyle now, you can work to prevent the chronic diseases that are the leading causes of premature death and disability in our society.

- Get passionate about your children's health. Degenerative disease begins in childhood; therefore, prevention needs to begin in childhood. As parents, we have a responsibility to set our children on the road to lifelong health. Help them develop the habits that will keep them healthy lifelong.

- Get smart – become a student of health. Learn all you can about what it takes to be healthy today and what it takes to stay healthy lifelong. Get your information from multiple, reliable sources: from friends, health-care professionals, books, magazines, television and radio programs, and from Internet sites you trust. Don't believe everything you read or hear. Remember the adage, "If it sounds too good to be true, it probably is." If and when you question someone's advice, follow up. Get a second or third opinion and compare.

- Get good health-care professionals on your team. Find a doctor who knows how to help you stay healthy. As noted earlier, too many health-care professionals practice reactive medicine. They give you no advice until you're sick, and then they treat you with drugs or surgery; largely because that's how they were trained in medical school. This isn't health care – it's disease management; too little, too late. Find a doctor who practices proactive (preventive) medicine. Find a doctor who knows how to help you and your family stay healthy in the long-term. Work with a doctor who can give you personalized, scientifically-based, comprehensive advice on what you need to do to optimize your health today and what you need to do over the long term.

- Get committed. The information you glean as a student of health and the advice you get from your health-care practitioner will undoubtedly direct you toward making certain lifestyle changes, such as eating a healthier diet, getting more exercise, and quitting a bad habit or two. You need to commit to making those changes. You have to follow through, and you should act now. Don't procrastinate. It's never too early to embark on the road to improved health. And it is never too late, as long as you do it today.

Stage II
Implementing Your Program for Long-Term Health

Implementation of your program for long-term health involves designing a lifestyle program that fits your health needs, and then putting that program into daily practice. Here are my recommendations for action:

Eat for Long-Term Good Health

First, eat the best diet you possibly can. Learn which foods are good for you and which are not. This is an absolutely essential requirement for long-term health and one that is largely abandoned today, primarily for lack of time. We have pushed mealtimes to the back burners of our lives, and many of us literally look at having to eat as an inconvenience. Slow down and take time to eat properly. Don't be in such a hurry to die young. Here are my simple guidelines for healthy eating. They follow the L-E-A-N Food Pyramid that appears on the following page.

- Eat a diet that is rich in plant-based foods and low in acid-forming, animal-based foods. As I like to say, eat low on the food chain. The most important message that comes out of hundreds of population-based studies linking diet and health is that diets rich in fruits, vegetables, and complex carbohydrates (fiber) from whole grains are central to reducing your risk of degenerative disease, particularly heart disease, cancer, and type 2 diabetes.

L·E·A·N Food Pyramid

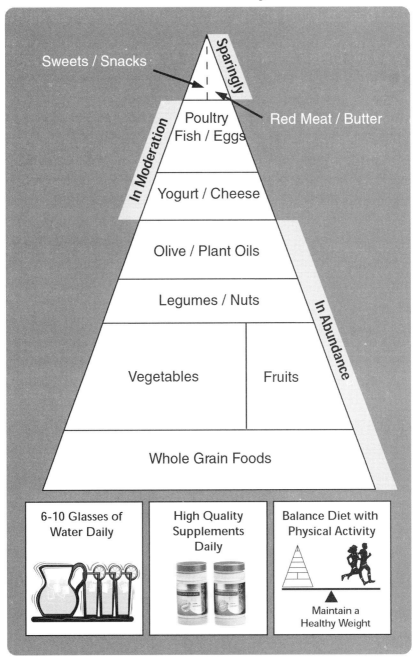

- Aim for 7 to 10 servings of fruits and vegetables per day – and eat in technicolor – select brightly colored red, orange, purple, and blue fruits and vegetables. Include lots of dark green, leafy vegetables. These are all rich sources of dietary fiber, vitamins, and minerals. Most importantly, they are a rich source of the diverse array of supplemental antioxidants that our cells need for healthy function, maintenance, and repair.

- Make whole grains and whole-grain products your primary source of carbohydrates. These foods are not only rich in fiber, vitamins, and minerals, but they tend to be low-glycemic, helping you to avoid the spikes in blood glucose and insulin that can contribute to overeating, obesity, diabetes, and heart disease.

- Round out your daily diet with several servings of legumes, seeds, and nuts to provide complete protein and healthy fats, as well as additional complex carbohydrate and fiber.

- Eat a diet that is relatively low in fat (less than 30 percent of calories) and, in particular, saturated animal fats, hydrogenated (trans-) fats, and rancid or oxidized fats. Instead, make sure that the fats you do consume are healthy ones: monounsaturated fats from olive oil and protected polyunsaturated (omega-3 and omega-6) fats from select vegetable oils, flax oil, and cold-water fish.

- Consume dairy products sparingly, if at all. Remember, plants are the intended source of calcium, not milk. But consider yogurt as a source of probiotic bacteria and flavorful cheese as a condiment.

- Eat meat sparingly. Select lean cuts of poultry and high-quality fish. Minimize consumption of red meat (treat it as a condiment), and avoid meat from some of the oceanic game fish (e.g. swordfish) that are known to concentrate mercury and other heavy metals.

- In general, eat fresh, uncooked or only lightly cooked foods. Limit consumption of processed, highly-refined foods, packaged foods and fast foods – the convenience isn't worth it. In particular, avoid snack foods, candy, soda pop, and other fat-, sugar-, and salt-laden junk. These "foods" tend to be calorie-rich, nutrient-poor, and high-glycemic, all of which contribute to overeating, obesity, diabetes, and heart disease.

- Drink plenty (6 to 10 glasses) of purified water each day; between, not during, meals. Mineral water – without gas – is acceptable; but remember, plants are your intended source of minerals, not water.

- Eat slowly and chew your food thoroughly. Give thanks for your life-sustaining nutrients.

- Balance the calories you consume through a healthy diet with the calories you burn through physical exercise to maintain a healthy weight.

Add High-Quality Supplementation

Second, to complement your healthy diet, take high-quality nutritional supplements to guarantee your intake of the essential nutrients. Select a supplement that is complete, one that contains the full array of essential vitamins, minerals, and antioxidants necessary for long-term health. And select a supplement that provides these nutrients at the advanced daily doses shown to prevent the chronic nutrient deficiencies that predispose us to degenerative diseases. Also, supplement your diet with additional fiber and with additional omega-3 fatty acids. We don't get the levels of fiber that we need from diet alone. Moreover, make sure that the supplements you choose are manufactured according the highest standards for quality and with uncompromised concern for safety.

To receive the critically important amount of vitamin E necessary for optimal health, you would have to consume one and a half pounds of sunflower seeds per day, which might be practical if you were a parrot; or drink a quart of safflower oil (just saying that makes my stomach a little uneasy); or eat two and a half pounds of almonds or a 5-pound bag of wheat germ in one day!

To receive the same amount of powerful antioxidants, called proanthocyanidins, you could try drinking ten glasses of grape juice or a bottle of red wine a day, but I recommend against it. Why these enormous quantities? Because as much as 70 percent of the nutrient value of these foods is lost through harvesting, transporting, processing, and packaging. Eating high-quality foods is important, but supplementation is essential today.

Exercise Regularly

Third, get on a program of regular exercise. The human body was designed for locomotion, and keeping it moving is the best thing you can do for it. "Use it or lose it" may be a cliché, but it is still true. Whatever else you do that is good for your body will be augmented and amplified by general physical fitness.

Physical activity is clearly linked with long-term health and reduced risk of heart disease, type 2 diabetes, osteoporosis, and some cancers. The amount and type of exercise that is right for you will greatly depend on your age, physical condition, dietary habits, weight management needs, and personal fitness goals. If you are uncertain where to begin or if, in particular, you are in relatively poor shape, work with your doctor or an experienced fitness trainer to get started. A good physical fitness program will do the following:

- Promote cardiovascular fitness

- Maintain flexibility

- Slow the loss of muscle mass and muscle tone with age

- Promote the circulation of the lymphatic system that is essential to flushing toxins out of the body

Assess Your Lifestyle

Fourth, avoid unhealthy habits. If you smoke, quit. If you drink alcohol, do so in moderation. If you drink alcohol to excess, or if you are addicted to harmful drugs, seek treatment. And again, do it today. Don't postpone these important actions for even an hour.

Minimize Exposure to Environmental Toxins

Fifth, identify the toxic substances in your life and do everything in your power to avoid them:

- Whenever possible, eat organically produced foods (fruits, vegetables, grains, nuts, and meats)

- Wash or peel fruits and vegetables

- Have your house inspected by a qualified safety engineer who can alert you to the presence of lead-based paints, radon gas, latent pesticides, and so forth

- Consult with a qualified, metal-free dentist about the hazards of mercury amalgam fillings

- Ensure that you have been properly trained in the handling of potentially hazardous materials that may exist in the home or at work

Reduce Stress

And sixth, eliminate, whenever possible, the causes of stress in your life. As William Shakespeare said, "There is nothing either good or bad, but thinking makes it so" (*Hamlet*, act 2, scene 2). The mind and the body are not separate, as Western thinking has it. They are inextricably intertwined. A healthy body is simply impossible without mental health, and good physical health can never be fully appreciated without a positive mental attitude.

The Mind-Body Connection

Much has been written through the ages and in recent years concerning the self-fulfilling prophecy. A self-fulfilling prophecy is a statement that is neither true nor false, but is capable of becoming true if it is believed. The mind has difficulty distinguishing an event that is real from one that has been vividly imagined. That is why the concepts of faith and belief are so important.

Science and religion are very closely allied in the implications resulting from studies of the brain during the past few decades. Although we have much to learn in understanding the mechanisms in the brain and central nervous system, we are aware of the inextricable relationship between psyche and soma – mind and body. There is a definite reaction in the body to the thoughts and concerns of the mind. What the mind harbors, the body manifests in some way.

For example, when our fears and worries turn into anxiety, we suffer distress. The distress activates the endocrine system in our bodies, and the production of hormones and antibodies changes. Our natural immune system becomes less active, and our resistance levels are lowered. We become more vulnerable to outside bacteria, viruses, and other environmental hazards – including free radicals – which are always present.

About the time I founded Gull Laboratories, some of the breakthrough research involving the mind-body relationship was taking place. Scientists already knew that hormones play an important role in regulating certain of our biological processes. Adrenaline is the hormone that enables us to fight or flee in the face of perceived danger, or in response to a call for peak physical performance. We are witness to these activities during athletic performances and hear about miraculous power surges every so often, such as grandmothers lifting cars and firemen making impossible rescues.

More recent discoveries have revealed that morphine-like hormones, called endorphins, are manufactured in our bodies to block pain and produce a "natural high." You are, no doubt, familiar with the placebo effect (*placebo* literally means "I shall please.") Placebos are inert substances usually given to volunteers, along with experimental drugs. By measuring the difference in responses between the powerless placebo and the drug, the drug's true effect is determined. One study conducted by the University of California involved a group of volunteers who had just had their wisdom teeth extracted. Some of the subjects received morphine to alleviate their pain. The others received a placebo that they believed to be morphine. Many of the placebo recipients said they experienced dramatic relief from their pain; however, when a drug was given to them that blocks the effects of endorphins (such as naloxone) the pain returned almost immediately.

The test confirmed something that is very important to understand. When a placebo is given, and the individual believes he or she is getting relief, the brain releases chemicals to substantiate the belief. In many respects, the placebo effect is an act of faith.

Here is a power which every person has, but which few people consciously use. As a positive influence, faith is the promise of the realization of things hoped for and unseen. As a negative influence, it is the premonition of our deepest fears and unseen darkness. There really is no such thing as a lack of faith. There is simply the replacement of faith with its opposite – despair.

That's why it is so important to gain knowledge about your health from credible sources and to remain optimistic and hopeful about the future. Establishing psychospiritual balance in your life will help you to do the following:

- Maintain a winning attitude

- Foster loving relationships

- Embrace happiness

Stage III
Maintaining Your Commitment to Lifelong Health

Too many of us become passionate about health, make commitments to live healthier lives, and enthusiastically embark on programs to improve eating habits, lose weight, get more exercise, reduce stress, and so forth – only to quit a few weeks or months, or perhaps a year or two later. The statistics on successful, long-term weight loss are sobering and indicative of lifestyle change as a whole. Fewer than 5 percent of people who embark on weight-loss programs, and lose significant weight at first, actually keep it off for more than 3 years. The rest gain the weight back – and many rebound, putting on more weight than they lost in the first place. There is no doubt about it. Changing lifelong habits – fundamentally changing the way we live and adopting new behavior patterns – is incredibly difficult, particularly when the payoff – good health during your senior years – may be decades away.

There is also no doubt about this – taking charge of your health is a lifelong undertaking. To be successful, you have to actively maintain your commitment to health for the rest of your life. This doesn't mean you have to live every day perfectly. It doesn't mean you have to beat yourself up when you slip up. To the contrary, I look at maintaining a few indulgences as a part of maintaining a rich, fulfilling, and happy life. I also look at my indulgences as indulgences – as special things that I get to do in moderation only on occasion and in a way that keeps them special. It's a matter of perspective and of balance.

Making a lifelong commitment to health means making the pursuit of health a way of life. For me, this was relatively easy. As the founder of Gull Laboratories, USANA Health Sciences, and Sanoviv, I have devoted my professional life to issues of human health. I continue to read books on health and articles in medical journals virtually every day. For many, maintaining a lifelong commitment is not easy.

Clearly, this is one of the biggest challenges in preventive health care: How do we encourage people to make necessary lifestyle changes for the long term? I wish I had the answer. I don't. I know that some don't find their commitment to health until after suffering a nonfatal heart attack or experiencing some other brush with death. Others succeed by joining health-related support groups, communities of people who share common goals and support one another in making valuable lifestyle changes. USANA is one example. There are many ways to succeed in this endeavor, and I remain optimistic that most people who develop a true passion for health will find a method that works for them.

This optimism is fundamental to my dream of a world free of pain and suffering, a world free of chronic degenerative disease. Take charge of your health. Share my vision.

Epilogue

Life is a wonderful celebration. To me, nothing is more beautiful than a healthy life in full bloom.

We've spent some time examining the problems we face in trying to attain true health and spending our lives with our bodies and minds functioning fully and harmoniously, as our Creator intended. We've talked about the toxic cradle and the need to protect ourselves against oxidative damage from the environment and against nutrient deficiency from our lifestyle choices, in an industrialized society in which convenience dominates our habits.

Now I'd like to concentrate on the celebration of life. The title of this book has a double meaning. While I see human cells as "invisible miracles" in their incredible ability to replicate and heal themselves, I see something much more profound and mysterious at work. Each cell has a distinct function, and yet, within every cell is all the information necessary to produce the unique person you see in the mirror every day. This is indeed miraculous; however, the real miracle is that the cells' activities are too complex to be explained – and they could not have come about by accident or chance assembly.

The definition of *miracle* is an event that appears inexplicable by the laws of nature and so is held to be supernatural in origin, or an act of God. A fitting synonym of *miracle* is *wonder*, and if any events have caused me more wonder in my life than my experiences in growing healthy cells, they would have to be the lives of my two children, David and Julie.

Miracles occur as acts of creation and also as events involving healing, regeneration, and renewal. I have witnessed them with my own eyes, especially associated with anecdotal testimonies provided by associates and families of USANA Health Sciences over the past decade and, more dramatically, with patients at Sanoviv Medical Retreat. These miracles come from the power of the body to heal itself through the remarkable ingenuity and creativity of the cells. Today's medical advances are sometimes called miracles, but I don't think these achievements can match, for a moment, what the cell does as a matter of routine.

The greatest invisible miracle of all is the existence of life, itself. According to the laws of physics, it should not be possible. The exquisite organization of every cell and every living organism appears to contradict scientific logic. Living matter involves forces we are unable to comprehend. Although we are able to artfully, articulately, and passionately theorize about life, we can't begin to understand the miracle responsible for our creation.

We stand in awe of the Rocky Mountains, the Pacific Ocean, the giant redwoods and the galaxies above us; and yet, did not the same creative genius breathe life into each of us? I humbly admit that I am awestruck by the miracle of our creation. If a church, synagogue, or mosque is your man-made house of worship, then the natural world where life abounds can be natural churches without walls or ceilings. Forging an authentic and regular relationship with our natural world is a rich and rewarding way to capture the spiritual moment. Memories of my boyhood on the plains of North Dakota and my subsequent travels throughout the world exploring our amazing planet, are precious to me for so many reasons – among them are the vivid appreciation and wonder for the natural world I have discovered.

A truly spiritual person, I believe, is not addicted to distraction and can easily spend a part of his or her days in solitude and quiet reflection. It's difficult – living as we do in a drive-through world – but we can make the choice to replenish and renew ourselves. We do it through a heightened and more creative appreciation for our lives. We do it through gratitude and optimism. We do it through contributing to the health and well-being of all people, and we do it through sustaining an ongoing relationship with nature.

When we are close to the earth, we have a much greater tendency to care for it. When we care for it, we're more likely to care for our fellow human beings, who are sustained by it. Nature provides us an opportunity to reflect and access what is godly and spiritual within ourselves and the larger world.

Nearly two centuries ago, the industrial revolution was sweeping the world, just as the information revolution is today. For some reason, this was also the moment in history when people really seemed to become aware of nature for the first time. It was as if trees and mountain peaks had somehow been invisible, until factories started to be built. Suddenly, we started to see by con-

trast what had been there all along. Suddenly, there was a great
flowering of nature-based poetry, painting, and music.

Perhaps, something like that is happening right now, as we
enter this new era of postindustrial society. Perhaps, by realizing
what we have done to threaten our own existence by our choices,
we will awaken to a new appreciation for the miracle of life. The
lines written by the English poet William Blake almost two hundred years ago, seem uncannily relevant:

> To see a world in a Grain of Sand
> And a heaven in a Wild Flower,
> Hold Infinity in the palm of your hand
> And Eternity for an hour.

Blake's poem serves as a preamble to a sacred truth – not
just for our connection with nature, but also for the intimate and
personal sense of spirituality that comes from the miracle of our
creation. I feel the presence of my Creator when I stand above the
smog on a mountaintop on a clear, crisp night, tracing the constel-
lations with an extended finger and marveling at the uncountable
billions of stars that lie within our Milky Way and the galaxies
beyond.

I feel it as I look into my microscope and see the uncountable billions of cells that go about the business of life as do com-
muters in heavy traffic every day.

I feel it when I walk quietly, luxuriously spending a solid
hour doing nothing but peering into the tidal pools among the
rocks below Sanoviv. I sense it as I picnic in the woods or in a
park, watching the wind play tag with the clouds and the leaves
on a tree, bird-watching, walking in the rain, or plying the emer-
ald-green waters of the Caribbean.

In the immensity of nature, I sense my own insignificance; that I am not the center of the universe. My omnipotent Creator is the center. And each living entity is a member of the Maestro's orchestra.

I believe in the beauty and harmony of life, with the utmost confidence that we are here by design, not by accident or aberration. Were you to look through the Palomar telescope in the mountains near San Diego at the wonders of the universe that cannot be seen by the naked eye, you would no doubt think to yourself, *What divine order!* The ancient Greeks looked up and called it *cosmos*, or universal order. The dividing of the human cell, as it was meant to do in optimal health, could also be referred to as *cosmos*, the universal order within. When the cells are damaged and cannot repair and regenerate themselves properly, the Greek term *chaos*, or universal disorder, applies. Harmony was created for us, and we humans often cause chaotic results by our choices and actions. Sometimes, those results involve forces of nature beyond our comprehension. More often, they involve ignorance or apathy.

The gift of life is not a treasure hunt. Success can't be measured through the collection of material possessions. Happiness cannot be traveled to, owned, earned, or worn. Happiness is the spiritual experience of living every minute with love, grace, and gratitude. The treasure is within you. It needs only to be uncovered and discovered.

Ralph Waldo Emerson beautifully articulated the kernel of truth that you and I have been discussing together:

How do you measure success?
To laugh often and much;

To win the respect of intelligent people
and the affection of children.
To earn the appreciation of honest critics
and endure the betrayal of false friends;
To appreciate beauty;
To find the best in others;
To leave the world a bit better,
whether by a healthy child, a garden patch,
a redeemed social condition, or a job well done;
To know even one other life has breathed easier
because you have lived—
This is to have succeeded.

I hope you sense the passion and urgency I feel about what we've discussed in this brief reflection of my involvement with cellular nutrition, focusing primarily on the past decade. I am often asked why I'm so impatient and so engrossed in the plight of human health. It is difficult to sum up a mission in life in so few pages; I can say that when a life is created, although not given any guarantee of survival in the world, that life is as important as any other that has gone before or that will follow. Earlier in my career, my focus was on regaining optimal health for myself and family, our mission must now be to unravel the mysteries that will provide hope and health for future generations.

I am committed to doing all I can – to use all of my talents and resources while on this earth – to further God's purpose and to reveal more opportunities for every man, woman, and child to experience the wonder of invisible miracles.

May you love life, and live it to its fullest in happiness and health.

Notes

1   Eve Curie, Madame Curie. Translated by Vincent Sheean (New York, NY: Simon & Schuster, 1946), pp. 252-53.

2   C. Hoffman, Chronic Care in America: A 21st Century Challenge. (San Francisco, CA: Institute for Health and Aging, University of California at San Francisco, 1996), p. 8.

3   Ibid p. 63.

4   D. Waitley, The Psychology of Human Motivation. (Chicago, IL: Nightingale-Conant, 1997), p. 396.

5   C. Hoffman, op. cit. p. 63.

6   E. M. Gruenberg, "The Failures of Success." Milbank Quarterly 1977, 55:3-24.

7   C. Hoffman, op. cit. p. 24.

8   American Diabetes Association, "Type 2 Diabetes in Children and Adolescents." Pediatrics 2000, 105:671-680.

9   See, E. F. Caldin, Fast Reactions in Solution. (New York, NY: John Wiley & Sons, 1964).

10 G. S. Berenson, S. R. Srinivasan, W. Bao, et al. "Association between Multiple Cardiovascular Risk Factors and Atherosclerosis in Children and Young Adults: The Bogalusa Heart Study." New England Journal of Medicine 1998, 338:1650-56.

11 K. L. Muñoz, et al. "Food Intakes of US Children and Adolescents Compared with Recommendations." Pediatrics 1997, 100:323.

12 H. L. Needleman and P. J. Landrigan, Raising Children Toxic Free. (New York, NY: Farrar, Straus & Giroux, 1994).

13 L. Mott, et al., The Five Worst Threats to Children's Health, (New York, NY: National Resources Defense Council, 1997) (See, www.nrdc.org/health/kids/n5worst.asp).

14 Luciano Pavarotti, "Choose One Chair." Guideposts, March 1985, p. 40.

15 <http://www.bmtnews.org/bmt.book/chapter 2.html>

16 J. D. Porter, A. Chavez, J. Chen, et al., "Food, Nutrition and the Prevention of Cancer: A Global Perspective." American Institute for Cancer Research and the World Cancer Research Fund, report, September 1997.

17 Lyle MacWilliam, Comparative Guide to Nutritional Supplements. (Vernon, BC: MacWilliam Communications, Inc., 2001), p. 8.

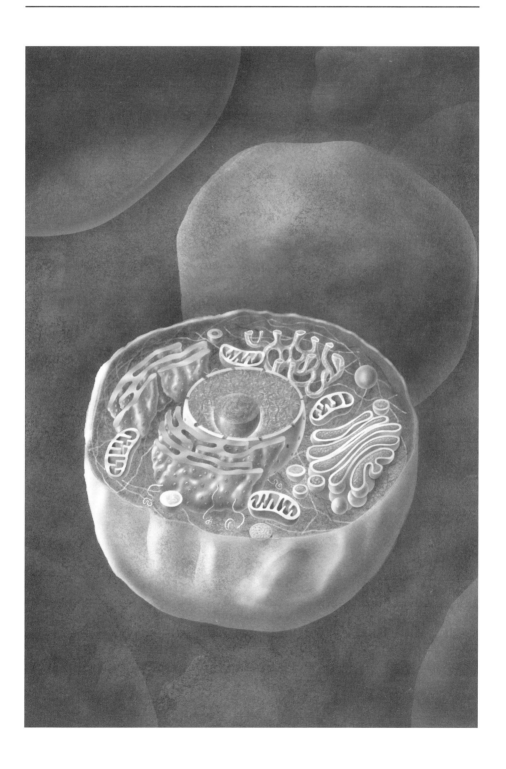